ST(P) MATHEMATICS 4

Teacher's Notes and Answer Book

L. Bostock, B.Sc.

formerly Senior Mathematics Lecturer, Southgate Technical College

S. Chandler, B.Sc.

formerly of the Godolphin and Latymer School

A. Shepherd, B.Sc.

Head of Mathematics, Redland High School for Girls

E. Smith, M.Sc.

Head of Mathematics, Tredegar Comprehensive School

Stanley Thornes (Publishers) Ltd

First published 1987 by
Stanley Thornes (Publishers) Ltd,
Educa House,
Old Station Drive,
Leckhampton Road,
CHELTENHAM GL53 0DN

British Library Cataloguing in Publication Data
ST(P) mathematics
    Book 4A Answers and teacher's notes
    1. Mathematics—1961—
    I. Bostock, L.
    510   QA39.2

    ISBN 0 85950 251 1

ST(P) MATHEMATICS will be completed as follows:

Published 1984	**ST(P) 1**	
	ST(P) 1	Teacher's Notes and Answer Book
	ST(P) 2	
Published 1985	**ST(P) 2**	Teacher's Notes and Answer Book
	ST(P) 3A	
	ST(P) 3B	
	ST(P) 3A	Teacher's Notes and Answer Book
	ST(P) 3B	Teacher's Notes and Answer Book
Published 1986	**ST(P) 4A**	
	ST(P) 4B	
	ST(P) 4A	Teacher's Notes and Answer Book
	ST(P) 4B	Teacher's Notes and Answer Book
To be published 1987	**ST(P) 5A**	(with answers)
	ST(P) 5B	(with answers)
In preparation	**ST(P) 5C**	

Typeset by Schooltext, CHELTENHAM
Printed in Great Britain by Ebenezer Baylis & Son Ltd, Worcester

INTRODUCTION

This book covers most of the work required for the written papers in the top level GCSE examinations. Book 5A completes and consolidates the course. The topics in this book are, in the main, common to the requirements of the five examining boards but there is some variation in syllabus content so it is sensible to check individual requirements.

Pupils who are clearly not going to attempt the highest level GCSE should not use this book. The parallel B series is designed for those attempting the middle level. Pupils taking the lowest level GCSE would be advised to progress from 3B to 5C.

Multiple choice questions are included in this book. Even if practice on these is not required for examination purposes, they are valuable teaching aids. Such questions often make pupils think about problems in a different way and, if done in class, often provoke useful discussions. Multiple choice questions are also an effective way to force reluctant pupils into thinking about the reasonableness, or otherwise, of an answer, especially if they are not given sufficient time to do much calculation.

Those questions that are double underlined, e.g. <u><u>2</u></u> , should be used cautiously if at all, with the less able. They are intended to give the brightest pupils food for thought but can easily damage the confidence of others. Questions which are single underlined, e.g. <u>2</u> , are extra, but not harder, questions. They can be used as extra practice, for faster workers or later for revision.

The text, though adequate, is brief and leaves ample scope for teachers to use their own methods and ideas, and to supplement the examples given. For a pupil who is revising a topic, the explanatory text is a useful reminder of the reasons for the methods followed.

Calculators should now be used fairly fully. In most cases, the required degree of accuracy is stated. When a result is required correct to three significant figures, then any intermediate working should be written down to four or five (no more) significant figures. In general, angles should be given correct to one decimal place and lengths calculated correct to three significant figures.

When pupils use calculators there is a strong tendency for them always to give answers correct to three significant figures or to give all the figures in the display, regardless of context. Pupils should be encouraged to think about the degree of accuracy appropriate to a given situation. They should also be encouraged to use appropriate units. For example they should realise the absurdity of giving the height of a tree to the nearest centimetre and the inappropriateness of giving the distance between Coventry and Birmingham in metres. There are questions in this book where the degree of accuracy required is not given and questions where the units required are not stated. These can be used for discussion.

The detailed notes that follow are only suggestions. Experienced teachers will have their own ideas on approach and order of content.

CHAPTER 1 Algebraic Fractions

EXERCISE 1a Revise factorisation of quadratics before this revision exercise.

1. $\dfrac{7x + 10}{12}$

2. $\dfrac{14x - 17}{20}$

3. $\dfrac{13x - 4}{10}$

4. $\dfrac{x + 4}{42}$

5. $\dfrac{6x + 11}{12}$

6. $\dfrac{7x + 17}{10}$

7. $\dfrac{7x - 2}{12}$

8. $\dfrac{19x - 1}{10}$

9. $\dfrac{x + 14}{12}$

10. $\dfrac{7x + 2}{30}$

11. $\dfrac{7x + 2}{6}$

12. $\dfrac{2x + 13}{12}$

13. $\dfrac{13}{4x}$

14. $\dfrac{3}{65a}$

15. $\dfrac{5x + 17}{(x + 3)(x + 4)}$

16. $\dfrac{2(x + 10)}{(x - 4)(x + 3)}$

17. $\dfrac{11}{2(x + 2)}$

18. $\dfrac{13}{3x}$

19. $\dfrac{1}{12a}$

20. $\dfrac{7x + 1}{(x + 3)(x - 1)}$

21. $\dfrac{5x - 53}{(x + 7)(x - 4)}$

EXERCISE 1b

1. $\dfrac{3x - 1}{(x + 1)(x - 1)}$

2. $\dfrac{3x - 1}{(x + 2)(x - 2)}$

3. $\dfrac{-(4x + 13)}{(x + 4)(x - 4)}$

4. $\dfrac{4x + 11}{(x + 3)(x - 3)}$

5. $\dfrac{x}{(x + 2)(x - 2)}$

6. $\dfrac{2x + 9}{(x + 1)(x - 1)}$

7. $\dfrac{3x - 17}{(x + 5)(x - 5)}$

8. $\dfrac{-(9x + 58)}{(x + 7)(x - 7)}$

9. $\dfrac{4x - 13}{(x + 4)(x - 4)}$

10. $\dfrac{3x - 8}{2x\,(x - 2)}$

11. $\dfrac{5x - 9}{3x\,(x + 3)}$

12. $\dfrac{5x - 6}{(x + 3)(x - 3)}$

EXERCISE 1c

1. $\dfrac{1}{x-1}$

2. $\dfrac{1}{2-x}$

3. $\dfrac{1}{x-4}$

4. $\dfrac{1}{x+1}$

5. $\dfrac{2}{x+1}$

6. $\dfrac{1}{2x+1}$

7. $\dfrac{-1}{x+3}$

8. $\dfrac{1}{(x+1)(x+2)}$

9. $\dfrac{1}{x-3}$

10. $\dfrac{1}{x-4}$

11. $\dfrac{1}{x-2}$

12. $\dfrac{2}{(x+1)(x-3)}$

13. $\dfrac{-3}{x+2}$

14. $\dfrac{-4}{2x+1}$

15. $\dfrac{2}{x+4}$

16. $\dfrac{3}{(x+2)(x+5)}$

EXERCISE 1d

1. $\dfrac{15x+11}{12}$

2. $\dfrac{5x-2}{20}$

3. $\dfrac{1}{6x}$

4. $\dfrac{2(3x+4)}{(x+2)(x-2)}$

5. $\dfrac{-(2x+13)}{(x-1)(x+2)(x-4)}$

6. $\dfrac{2}{x-2}$

7. $\dfrac{2}{(x-2)(x-4)}$

8. $\dfrac{1}{(2x-1)(3x+1)}$

EXERCISE 1e

1. 6

2. 8

3. 5

4. 12

5. 24

6. 20

7. 20

8. 14

9. 2

10. 4

11. 4

12. $\frac{1}{2}$

13. 2

14. 3

15. 3

16. $\frac{1}{3}$

17. 2

18. 3

19. 3

20. 2

21. −2

22. 2

23. 2

24. 4

25. 3

EXERCISE 1f

1. 2, 3

2. −5, 4

3. −1, 5

10. $-5\frac{1}{6}$, 4

11. $-2\frac{1}{2}$, 5

12. 4, 20

4. −3, 4

5. $-\frac{7}{2}$, 3

6. 4, 10

13. $-1\frac{1}{2}$, $-1\frac{1}{4}$

14. 1, 2

7. −1, −3

8. −3, 4

9. $\frac{1}{2}$, 3

15. $-4\frac{1}{3}$, 2

16. 8, 1

CHAPTER 2   Sets

No previous knowledge is assumed although much of the work is covered in Book 1. Even if sets were done earlier, a thorough revision of notation is desirable.

Many of the early exercises in this chapter are suitable for discussion in class. The better pupils will progress very rapidly, especially if sets were studied in Book 1.

EXERCISE 2a

1. a) {teachers in my school}   b) {books I have read}

3. a) {odd numbers 1 to 9 inclusive}
   b) {days of the week when we go to school}
     or {days of the week except Saturday and Sunday}

4. a) {European countries},   France
   b) {multiples of 10},   60

5. a) {2, 3, 5, 7, 11}   b) {A, B, E, G, L, R}

EXERCISE 2b

1. John ∈ {boys' names}
2. English ∈ {school subjects}
3. June ∉ {days of the week}
4. Jaguar ∈ {British cars}
5. Monday ∉ {domestic furniture}
6. Curtain ∉ {crockery}
7. False
8. False
9. True
10. True
11. True

EXERCISE 2c

1. Infinite
2. Finite
3. Finite
4. Infinite
5. Finite

6. Infinite
7. Finite
8. 5
9. 3
10. 8

11. 6
12. 5

13. 21
14. 8

15. 11
16. 11

EXERCISE 2d

1. No
2. Yes

3. Yes
4. No

5. Yes
6. No

7. Yes
8. Yes

9. No
10. No

EXERCISE 2e   Some teachers may prefer to introduce the universal set earlier than this.

1. $\mathcal{E}$ = {cutlery}

2. $\mathcal{E}$ = {integers from 10 to 40 inclusive} or {multiples of 5}

3. $\mathcal{E}$ = {integers less than 25} or {integers}

4. A = {2, 3, 5, 7, 11, 13, 17, 19}, B = {3, 6, 9, 12, 15, 18}

5. A = {a, e, i, o, u}, B = {H, Y, M, N, S}

6. A = {11, 13, 17, 19, 23, 29}, B = {12, 15, 18, 21, 24, 27, 30}, C = {12, 16, 20, 24, 28}

7. A = {1, 2, 3, 4, 6, 12}, B = {2, 3, 5, 7, 11, 13}, C = {6, 12}

8. $\mathcal{E}$ = {A, C, F, I, L, N}, A = {A, C, I, L, N}, B = {A, F, L, N}

9. A = {5, 10, 15, 20}, B = {7, 14}, C = {4, 8, 12, 16, 20}

EXERCISE 2f

1. {Jill, Audrey} ,   {Jill, Janet} ,   {Audrey, Janet}

2. A = {2, 4, 6, 8, 10, 12, 14}, B = {2, 3, 5, 7, 11, 13}, C = {3, 6, 9, 12, 15}
   Yes, 2

3. a) {London, Paris, Rome} for example
   b) {Clyde, Severn, Thames} for example
   c) {India, Australia, New Zealand} for example

4. B = {6, 12, 18}, C = {2}, D = {14, 16, 18, 20}

EXERCISE 2g   **1.** a)   b) Yes

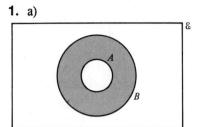

2.

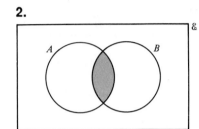

4.

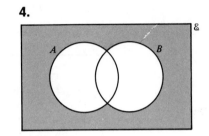

3.

5.

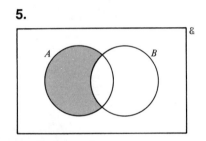

6. {pupils who are my friends who do not like coming to school}

7. {pupils who are not my friends and do not like coming to school}

8. {pupils who like coming to school and are my friends}

9. {pupils who are my friends and pupils who do not like coming to school}

10. {pupils who are not my friends and do not like coming to school and pupils who are my friends and like coming to school}

11. {all pupils except those of my friends who like coming to school}

EXERCISE 2h

1.

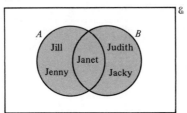

$A \cup B$ = {Jill, Jenny, Janet, Judith, Jacky}

2.

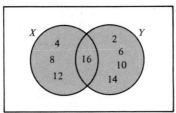

$X \cup Y$ = {2, 4, 6, 8, 10, 12, 14, 16}

3.

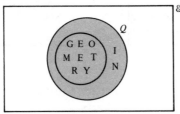

$P \cup Q$ = {G, E, O, M, E, T, R, Y, I, N}

4.

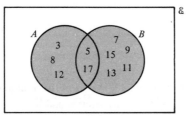

$A \cup B$ = {3, 5, 7, 8, 9, 11, 12, 13, 15, 17}

5.

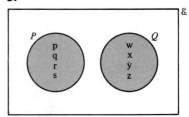

$P \cup Q$ = {p, q, r, s, w, x, y, z}

6. a)

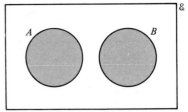

$A \cup B$ = {trapeziums and parallelograms}

(Some people may consider that parallelograms are a special case of trapeziums, in which case A should be within B)

b)

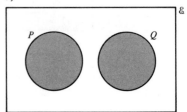

$P \cup Q$ = {angles that are either obtuse or reflex}

EXERCISE 2i   **1.**

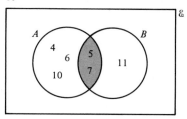

$$A \cap B = \{5, 7\}$$

4.

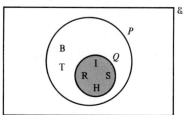

$$P \cap Q = \{H, I, R, S\}$$

2.

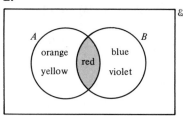

$$A \cap B = \{red\}$$

5.

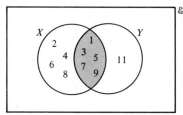

$$X \cap Y = \{1, 3, 5, 7, 9\}$$

3.

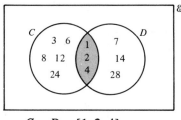

$$C \cap D = \{1, 2, 4\}$$

6.

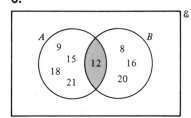

$$A \cap B = \{12\}$$

EXERCISE 2j   **1.** a) {Lenny, Sylvia}

b) {Richard, Adam}

c) {Scott, Jack, Pat}

2. a) {David, Joe, Tariq, Paul}

b) {Tariq, Paul}

c) {Claude, Alun, Clive}

3. a) {Emma, Majid, Roger, Sean, Ann}

b) {Emma, Majid, Roger}

c) {Sean, Ann}

4.

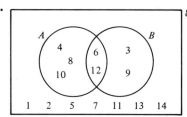

a) {6, 12}

b) {3, 9}

5.

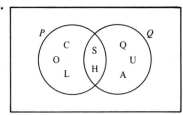

a) S, H

b) C, O, L, Q, U, A

c) C, O, L

6.

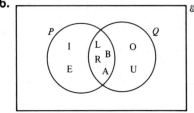

a) $P \cap Q$ = {A, B, L, R};
   letters that appear in both words

b) $P \cup Q$ = {A, B, E, I, L, O, R, U};
   letters that appear in either word
   or in both words

7.

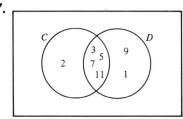

a) $C \cap D$ = {3, 5, 7, 11}

b) $C \cup D$ = {1, 2, 3, 5, 7, 9, 11}

8.

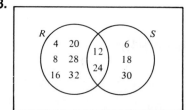

a) $R \cup S$ = {4, 6, 8, 12, 16, 18, 20,
                24, 28, 30, 32}

b) $R \cap S$ = {12, 24}

EXERCISE 2k

1. $A' = \{10, 20\}$
2. $B' = \{5, 6, 11\}$
3. $V' = \{\text{consonants}\}$
4. $P' = \{\text{vowels}\}$
5. $A' = \{\text{Sunday, Tuesday, Thursday, Saturday}\}$
6. $X' = \{\text{adults}\}$
7. $M' = \{\text{foreign motor cars}\}$
8. $S' = \{\text{female tennis players}\}$
9. $C' = \{\text{Belfast}\}$
10. $D' = \{\text{quadrilaterals which are not squares}\}$

11. $E' = \{\text{adults 80 years old or younger}\}$
12. $F' = \{\text{female doctors}\}$
13. $\& = \{\text{homes}\}$
14. $\& = \{\text{letters of the alphabet}\}$
15. $\& = \{a, b, c, d, e, f, g, h, i, j\}$
16. a)

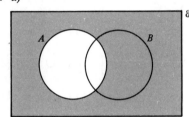

b)

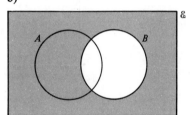

EXERCISE 2l

1.

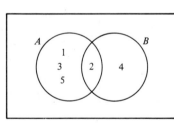

a) $A' = \{4\}$
b) $B' = \{1, 3, 5\}$
c) $A \cup B = \{1, 2, 3, 4, 5\}$
d) $(A \cup B)' = \{\ \}$ or $\emptyset$
e) $A' \cup B' = \{4, 1, 3, 5\}$

2.

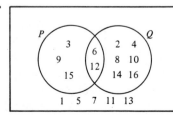

a) $P' = \{1, 2, 4, 5, 7, 8, 10, 11, 13, 14, 16\}$
b) $Q' = \{1, 3, 5, 7, 9, 11, 13, 15\}$
c) $P \cup Q = \{2, 3, 4, 6, 8, 9, 10, 12, 14, 15, 16\}$
d) $(P \cup Q)' = \{1, 5, 7, 11, 13\}$
e) $P' \cap Q' = \{1, 5, 7, 11, 13\}$

3.

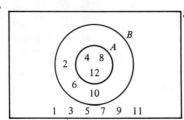

a) $A' = \{1, 2, 3, 5, 6, 7, 9, 10, 11\}$
b) $B' = \{1, 3, 5, 7, 9, 11\}$
c) $A \cup B = \{2, 4, 6, 8, 10, 12\}$
d) $(A \cup B)' = \{1, 3, 5, 7, 9, 11\}$
e) $A' \cap B' = \{1, 3, 5, 7, 9, 11\}$

4.

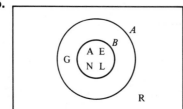

a) $P' = \{10, 11, 13, 14, 15, 17, 18,$
$19, 21, 22, 23, 25\}$
b) $Q' = \{11, 12, 13, 14, 16, 17, 18,$
$19, 21, 22, 23, 24\}$
c) $P \cup Q = \{10, 12, 15, 16, 20, 24,$
$25\}$
d) $(P \cup Q)' = \{11, 13, 14, 17, 18,$
$19, 21, 22, 23\}$
e) $P' \cap Q' = \{11, 13, 14, 17, 18,$
$19, 21, 22, 23\}$

5.

a) $A' = \{R\}$
b) $B' = \{G, R\}$
c) $A \cap B = \{A, E, L, N\}$
d) $A \cup B = \{A, E, G, L, N\}$
e) $(A \cap B)' = \{G, R\}$
f) $A' \cap B' = \{R\}$

6.

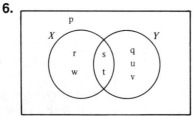

a) $X' = \{p, q, u, v\}$
b) $Y' = \{p, r, w\}$
c) $X' \cap Y' = \{p\}$
d) $X \cup Y = \{q, r, s, t, u, v, w\}$
e) $(X \cup Y)' = \{p\}$
    $X' \cap Y'$ and $(X \cup Y)'$

7.

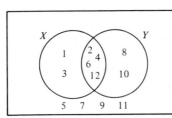

a) $X' = \{5, 7, 8, 9, 10, 11\}$
b) $Y' = \{1, 3, 5, 7, 9, 11\}$
c) $X' \cap Y' = \{5, 7, 9, 11\}$
d) $X' \cup Y' = \{1, 3, 5, 7, 8, 9, 10, 11\}$
e) $X \cup Y = \{1, 2, 3, 4, 6, 8, 10, 12\}$
f) $(X \cup Y)' = \{5, 7, 9, 11\}$
   $X' \cap Y'$ and $(X \cup Y)'$

8. a)

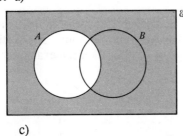

b)

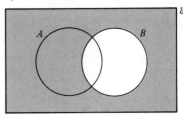

c)

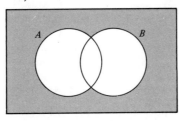

d)

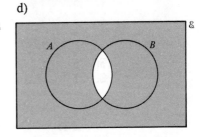

e)

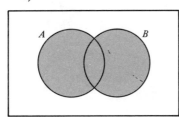

f)

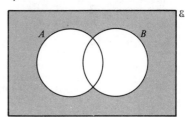

9.

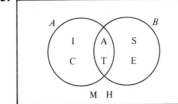

a) $A' = \{E, H, M, S\}$
b) $B' = \{C, H, I, M\}$
c) $A \cup B = \{A, C, E, I, S, T\}$
d) $(A \cup B)' = \{H, M\}$
e) $A' \cup B' = \{C, E, H, I, M, S\}$
f) $A' \cap B' = \{H, M\}$

10. a) P' = {pupils in my class without compasses}

b) Q' = {pupils in my class without protractors}

c) $P' \cap Q'$ = {pupils in my class with neither compasses nor protractors}

d) $(P \cup Q)'$ = {pupils in my class with neither compasses nor protractors}

e) $P \cup Q$ = {pupils in my class with either compasses and/or a protractor}

EXERCISE 2m   From No 7 onwards, the number of elements in the set are given; the actual elements are not listed in the Venn diagram. This distinction needs to be made very clear with plenty of discussion and examples.

	$n(A)$	$n(B)$	$n(A \cup B)$	$n(A \cap B)$
1.	5	7	9	3
2.	4	5	7	2
3.	3	6	7	2
4.	6	4	8	2
5.	4	3	6	1
6.	5	6	8	3

	$n(X)$	$n(Y)$	$n(X \cup Y)$	$n(X \cap Y)$
7.	9	7	12	4
8.	5	2	7	0
9.	13	10	16	7
10.	12	12	20	4

	$n(A)$	$n(B)$	$n(A')$	$n(B')$	$n(A \cup B)$	$n(A \cap B)$	$n(A' \cup B')$	$n(A \cap B)'$
11.	3	5	9	7	7	1	11	11
12.	3	1	5	7	4	0	8	8
13.	6	5	4	5	8	3	7	7
14.	11	13	15	13	18	6	20	20
15.	8	5	6	9	10	3	11	11
16.	9	5	6	10	12	2	13	13

EXERCISE 2n   **1.** a) 3   b) 4   c) 12   d) 13
    2. a) 27   b) 14   c) 8   d) 19

3.

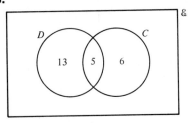

a) 11   b) 13   c) 19

4.

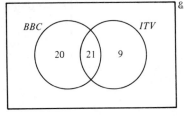

a) 41   b) 20   c) 29

5.

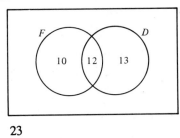

23

6.

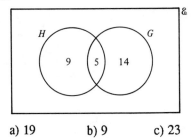

a) 19   b) 9   c) 23

7.

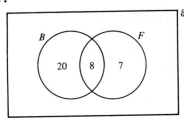

3

8. a) 8   b) 11   c) 23

9. a) 32   b) 23   c) 17

10.

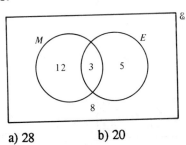

a) 28   b) 20

11.

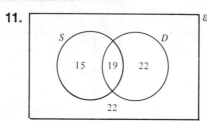

a) 15   b) 37   c) 22

12.

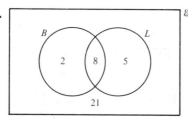

a) 15   b) 21   c) 7

13. a) 14   b) 19

EXERCISE 2p   Some of the questions in this exercise are very demanding. The good problem solvers will enjoy these.

1. a) 52   b) i) 38   ii) 9   iii) 21

2. a) 4   b) 8   c) 8   d) 9
$x = 5$,
    i) {pupils who are members of both the hockey team and the netball team}
    ii) {pupils who are members of the netball team but not members of the swimming team}
    iii) {pupils who are not members of the netball team}

3.

$A' \cap B$ is an empty set

4.

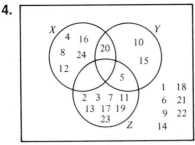

a) {4, 5, 8, 10, 12, 15, 16, 20, 24}
b) {2, 3, 5, 7, 11, 13, 17, 19, 23}
c) {1, 6, 9, 14, 18, 21, 22}
d) {5, 10, 15, 20}

5. a) {E, G, M, R, T}   b) 11

6.

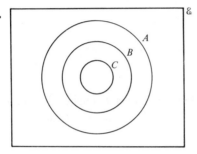

7.

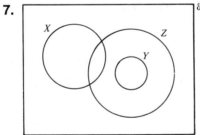

a) Isosceles right-angled triangles
b) Equilateral triangles
c) Equilateral triangles and right-angled triangles

8.

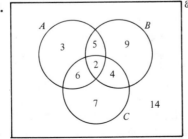

a) 23   b) 37   c) 14

9.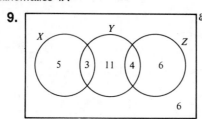

a) 0   b) 30   c) 17

10. a) 5   b) 16   c) 11   d) 0

11. a) 5   b) 26   c) 17   d) 7

12. (a), (b), (f)

CHAPTER 3   Volume and Mass ─────────────────

EXERCISE 3a   Revises earlier work but with harder examples. Calculators should be used and pupils encouraged to check results by estimation.

1. 35 700 cm³   **3.** 130 m³   **5.** 1680 mm²
2. 13.7 cm³   **4.** 432 cm³

6. a) 1 000 000 or 10⁶   b) 4 230 000 cm³
7. a) 1000   b) 0.628 cm³

8. 4.2 litres   **10.** 75 m³   **12.** 7.8 cm³
9. 48 000 cm³   **11.** 0.432 m³   **13.** 42 000 mm³

14. 13.3 cm   **16.** 0.625 cm   **18.** 3530 cm³
15. 2.29 m   **17.** 2.11 mm   **19.** 20 cm

20. a) 120 000 cm³ or 0.12 m³   b) 50 cm or 0.5 m
21. 864 cm³

EXERCISE 3b   Revises earlier work but with harder examples.

1. 2175 cm^3 **3.** 1920 cm^3 **5.** 55.44 m^3
2. 32 000 cm^3 **4.** 17.6 m^3 **6.** 0.66 cm^3

7. 0.88 cm^3 **9.** 0.72 m^3 **11.** 9 cm
8. 2580 cm^3 **10.** 1728 cm^3 **12.** 32 m^2

13. a) 44 cm^2 b) 9 cm
14. a) 12 cm   b) 60 cm^2 c) 20 cm
15. 26 cm
16. a) 0.05 cm   b) 0.5 mm
17. 14.4 cm
18. 144 cm^3
19. a) 47.1 cm^3 b) 2830 cm^3
20. a) 13 cm   b) 60 cm^2 c) 1200 cm^3
21. a) 2250 m^3 b) 0.03 m^3 c) 5 hrs 13 mins

VOLUME OF A PYRAMID

Nets for making solids to demonstrate that the volume of a pyramid is $\frac{1}{3}$ area of base × perpendicular height.

First Method

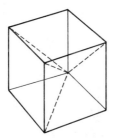 

A cube can be formed from three identical pyramids each with a square base

Net

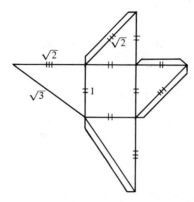

Start by drawing the square, then draw the two smaller triangles, finishing with the two larger triangles. Make sure the indicated lengths are equal.

Second Method

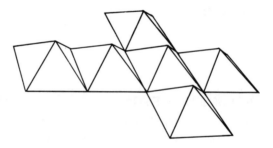

This will fold up into a cube with the vertices of the six pyramids at the centre.

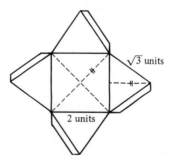

Make six pyramids and stick their bases to the six squares below.

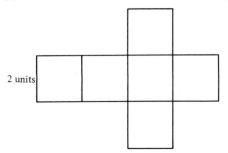

2 units

EXERCISE 3c

1. 72 cm³
2. 640 cm³
3. 80 cm³
4. 960 m³
5. 118 m³
6. 38.4 cm³

7. 256 cm³
8. a) 10 cm, 5 cm b) 12 cm c) 192 cm³
9. a) 7.50 cm b) 165 cm³

EXERCISE 3d

1. 71.4 g
2. 106 g
3. a) 19 800 g, 19.8 kg
4. 980 g
5. 618 g
6. 13.8 g

7. 17.2 g
8. 0.69 g
9. 8.9 g
10. 0.55 g
11. 2.5 g per cm³
12. 2.6 g per cm³
13. 62 cm³
14. 2450 cm³
15. 1990 g

16. a) 2.83 cm b) 90.5 cm³
    c) i) 1450 g ii) 1.45 kg d) £10 100 (to nearest £100)
17. a) 0.112 cm³ b) 0.392 g

EXERCISE 3e

1. B
2. D
3. B
4. C

CHAPTER 4   **Formulae**

The answers given are not the only possible version. For instance $z = x + \dfrac{y}{100}$ may be given as $z = \dfrac{100x + y}{100}$ and $p = 2l + 2b$ may be given as $p = 2(l + b)$

EXERCISE 4a

1. a) 95 p b) $C = 25x + 15y$

2. a) 40 ° b) $y = 180 - 2x$

3. $n = \dfrac{a+b}{2}$

4. $p = 2l + 2b$

5. $C = \dfrac{pm}{100}$

6. $C = A + nD$

7. $p = 10q$

8. $T = n + 1$

9. $t = 2n - 1$

10. $b = 3c + 10$

11. $z = x + \dfrac{y}{100}$

12. $s = 3n + 3$

EXERCISE 4b   Revise directed numbers.

1. a) 15   b) 14.4

2. a) –1   b) 2.575

3. a) $\frac{5}{8}$ b) 12

4. a) 77   b) 21.2

5. a) 63   b) 7.56

6. 452 cm²

7. 3.59 s

8. 330 cm²

9. 11 300 m or 11.3 km

10. 12.3 J

11. 23.1 m

EXERCISE 4c

1. a) 6   b) 3

2. 9

3. a) $\frac{3}{4}$ b) 1.8

4. a) 17   b) $2\frac{1}{3}$

5. a) 2   b) 1.6

6. a) 6   b) 0.25

7. $1\frac{5}{7}$

8. 22

9. a) 10 cm   b) 20 cm

10. 12 sides

11. a) 150 miles   b) 52 people

EXERCISE 4d

1. 2

2. –5

3. $9 - a$

4. $\dfrac{q}{6}$

5. $q - p$

6. $\dfrac{n}{m}$

7. $e + f$

8. $\dfrac{g}{h}$

9. $g + h$

10. $k - h$

11. $r = p - q$

12. $s = r + t$

13. $t = r - s$

14. $z = \dfrac{y}{x}$

15. $m = n - l$

16. $Q = \dfrac{P}{R}$

17. $a = 2s - b - c$

18. $r = \dfrac{C}{2\pi}$

19. $b = \dfrac{A}{l}$

20. $u = v - at$

EXERCISE 4e

1. 2

2. 4

3. 2

4. $1\frac{1}{2}$

5. $\dfrac{r-q}{P}$

6. $\dfrac{c-d}{b}$

7. $\dfrac{b+c}{a}$

8. $\dfrac{a-c}{b}$

9. $\dfrac{c-ab}{a}$

10. $\dfrac{2+pq}{P}$

11. $d = ab - c$

12. $a = \dfrac{c+d}{b}$

13. $q = \dfrac{1-pr}{p}$

14. $P = \dfrac{2+3Q}{3}$

15. $t = \dfrac{s-u}{7}$

16. $l = 2 + mn$

17. $m = \dfrac{l-2}{n}$

18. $P = \dfrac{4T-Q}{2}$

19. $p = \dfrac{m-mr}{r}$ or $p = \dfrac{m(1-r)}{r}$

20. $y = \dfrac{2+zx}{x}$

21. a) 45. 2   b) 11   c) $a = \dfrac{P-4b}{4}$ d) 11, yes

22. a) 1017.6   b) –2   c) $a = \dfrac{A-3nl}{3n}$ d) –2

23. a) 2.1   b) $\frac{1}{2}$ c) $y = \dfrac{x-z}{z}$ d) $\frac{1}{2}$

EXERCISE 4f In the worked example, as there is a choice, the answer may be of the form $x = \dfrac{d-c}{b-a}$

1. $2\frac{1}{2}$

2. $\frac{3}{5}$

3. $\frac{2}{5}$

4. 2

5. $\dfrac{c}{a-b}$

6. $\dfrac{b}{a-c}$

7. $\dfrac{2q}{p-r}$

8. $\dfrac{s}{p+t}$

9. $\dfrac{a-c}{b+d}$

10. $\dfrac{a-c}{b-d}$ or $\dfrac{c-a}{d-b}$

11. $\dfrac{p}{q+r+s}$

12. $\dfrac{a+b+d}{c}$

Questions 11 to 14 need careful attention with many examples

13. $\dfrac{c}{a+1}$

14. $\dfrac{4}{b-1}$

15. $\dfrac{d}{c-1}$

16. $\dfrac{a}{1-2a}$

17. $p = \dfrac{r}{q+s}$

18. $a = \dfrac{a}{b+c}$

19. $a = \dfrac{c}{b-d}$

20. $a = \dfrac{c-b}{x-y}$

21. $p = \dfrac{-qr}{q+r}$

22. $a = \dfrac{b}{c-1}$

23. $q = \dfrac{pr-p}{r+1} = \dfrac{p(r-1)}{r+1}$

24. $r = \dfrac{p+q}{p-q}$

25. 5

26. $\frac{2}{3}$

27. 10

28. $\dfrac{b}{a-b}$

29. $\dfrac{ab+c}{a}$

30. $\dfrac{ab}{b-a}$

31. $\dfrac{ac+bc}{b-a} = \dfrac{c(a+b)}{b-a}$

32. $\dfrac{cd-ab}{a-c}$

33. $q = \dfrac{pr}{1-p}$

34. $a = \dfrac{bc}{b-c}$

35. $s = \dfrac{ut}{2t+u}$

36. $n = \dfrac{ml}{1+m}$

37. $p = \dfrac{q}{q+r}$

38. $R = \dfrac{PQ}{P-Q}$

39. $b = \dfrac{ac}{a-c}$

40. $u = \dfrac{2st}{t-s}$

EXERCISE 4g   The difference between type (a) and type (b) in the worked example needs to be made clear.

1. 8

2. 5

3. $\frac{5}{2} = 2\frac{1}{2}$

4. $\frac{2}{3}$

5. $4\frac{1}{2}$

6. $2\frac{1}{2}$

7. $\frac{1}{8}$

8. 100

9. 1000

10. ± 12

11. 4

12. ± 11

13. ± 30

14. ± 10

15. -3

EXERCISE 4h

1. ± 2

2. $\pm\frac{5}{3}$

3. $\pm\sqrt{\dfrac{5}{3}}$

4. $\pm\sqrt{p}$

5. $\pm\sqrt{\dfrac{q}{p}}$

6. $\pm\dfrac{q}{\sqrt{p}}$

7. $\pm\sqrt{p+q}$

8. $\pm\sqrt{\dfrac{bc}{a}}$

9. 16

10. $\frac{4}{9}$

11. 27

12. a^2

13. $\dfrac{q^2}{p^2}$

14. $\dfrac{r^2}{p}$

15. p^2q

16. $16-a$

17. $p = \pm\dfrac{\sqrt{q}}{2}$

21. $A = C^2 - B$

18. $p = \dfrac{a^2}{4}$

22. $h = \dfrac{2D^2}{3}$

19. $a = b^2 - x$

23. $b = z - a$

20. $a = \pm\sqrt{c - b}$

24. $x = \pm\sqrt{b^2 - a^2}$

25. a) ± 3 b) ± 5

27. a) 4   b) 20

26. 3 seconds

   c) $Q = P^2 - R$ d) 20, Yes

EXERCISE 4i   It is most important that fractions are removed as soon as possible otherwise the solution is either unnecessarily complicated or, as often as not, wrong.

1. 24

5. pq

9. $a(c - b)$

2. $7\frac{1}{2}$

6. $\dfrac{pq}{q - p}$

10. $\dfrac{a^2 + b^2}{b - a}$

3. $1\frac{3}{5}$

7. $\dfrac{pr}{a}$

11. a

4. $2\frac{2}{5}$

8. $r(p + q)$

12. $\dfrac{bc}{a + b}$

13. $R = \dfrac{100I}{PT}$

17. $x = \dfrac{ab}{a + b}$

21. $l = \dfrac{gT^2}{4\pi^2}$

14. $n = \dfrac{2A}{a + l}$

18. $x = p + q + r$

22. $H = \dfrac{ht}{2h - t}$

15. $Q = 4P - R$

19. $x = \dfrac{s - r}{t}$

23. $X = \dfrac{-(b^2 + c)}{ba^2}$

16. $b = \dfrac{4a + 3c}{6}$

20. $q = \dfrac{4p}{a^2}$

24. $B = \dfrac{2aM + bL}{L}$

EXERCISE 4j   **1.** $t = \dfrac{v - u}{a}$

4. $h = \dfrac{2A}{a + b}$

2. $h = \dfrac{2A}{b}$

5. $f = \dfrac{uv}{u + v}$

3. $c = \pm\sqrt{a^2 - b^2}$

6. $a = \dfrac{2A - bh}{h}$

7. $v = \dfrac{2s - ut}{t}$

8. $t = \dfrac{2s}{u + v}$

9. $u = \dfrac{vf}{v - f}$

10. $a = \dfrac{v^2 - u^2}{2s}$

11. $h = \dfrac{A - \pi r^2}{\pi r}$

12. $u = \pm \sqrt{v^2 - 2as}$

13. $a = \pm \dfrac{\sqrt{v^2 + w^2 x^2}}{w}$

14. $h = \pm \dfrac{\sqrt{A^2 - \pi^2 r^4}}{\pi r}$

15. $u = \dfrac{2s - at^2}{2t}$

16. $a = \dfrac{2s - 2ut}{t^2}$

17. $p = \dfrac{2A}{qs - R}$

18. $u = \pm \sqrt{\dfrac{mv^2 - 2E}{m}}$

19. $g = \dfrac{4\pi^2 l}{T^2}$

20. $R = \dfrac{100A - 100P}{PT}$

EXERCISE 4k

1. $6\frac{4}{5}$

2. 7

3. $c = \dfrac{a^2 - b^2 d}{b^2}$

4. $T = \dfrac{100I}{PR}$

5. 7

EXERCISE 4l

1. -0.55

2. ± 6

3. $d = T(v - u)$

4. $p = \dfrac{q^2}{16}$

5. $b = \dfrac{ac}{c - a}$

EXERCISE 4m   **1.** C   **2.** C   **3.** A   **4.** C   **5.** D

CHAPTER 5   Graphs

A list of useful techniques for drawing curves was given in a previous book. These points are important and should be repeated. They are:
1. Do not take too few points. About ten are usually necessary.
2. To decide where to draw the x-axis, look at the range of y-values.
3. To decide where to draw the y-axis, look at the range of x-values.
4. In some questions most of the y-values are given but some have to be calculated. In this case always plot first those points that were given and from these, get an idea of the shape of the curve. Then plot the points that were calculated and see if they fit onto the curve you have in mind. If they do not, go back and check the calculations.

5. To draw a smooth curve to pass through the points, always turn the page into a position where the wrist is on the inside of the curve.

Some pupils can investigate the graph of $x = y^2$. Show that all we have done is interchange the x and y axes.

EXERCISE 5a

1. a) 3.25,　1.5　　　b) i) -0.30,　3.30　　　ii) 1,　2
2. a) -1,　2　　　b) i) 0.27,　3.73　ii) 2　iii) -0.24,　4.24
3. a) 4.65,　-0.65　　b) 5.79,　-1.79
4. a) 2,　3　　　b) -0.25　　　c) 0.4,　4.6
5. a) 5,　$x = 1$　　b) 2.1　　　c) -0.4,　2.4
6. a) $6\frac{1}{4}$,　$x = -\frac{3}{2}$　　b) 0.6,　-3.6

EXERCISE 5b

1. a) -1,　4　　　b) -1.7,　4.7　c) -1.5,　4.5　　d) 0.4,　2.6
2. a) -0.85,　4.85　b) 0.25,　3.7　c) -0.65,　4.6　d) -0.24,　4.24
   e) 0.59,　3.41
3. a) 1,　3　　　b) 3.7,　0.3　　c) 4.2,　-0.2　d) 5,　-1
4. a) 3.3,　-0.3　　　　　b) 3.6,　-0.6
   c) 4.2,　-1.2;　No, the line $y = 5$ does not intersect the graph
5. a) 5.4,　0.6;　$x^2 - 6x + 3 = 0$
   b) 4.4,　1.6
6. a) -1,　2　　　b) -1.8,　2.79
7. a) 1.9　　　　　b) 0.72,　2.78
8. a) -3.91,　0.9　　b) -3.31,　0.3,　$x^2 + 3x - 1 = 0$
9. a) No solutions　　b) -1.38,　1.7　　　c) -0.44,　0.77
10. -3.25,　1.24
11. -5.54,　0.54

EXERCISE 5c

1. a) $x^2 - x - 7 = 0$　　　　b) $x^2 - 2x - 5 = 0$
   c) $x^2 - 6x + 4 = 0$　　　d) $x^2 + 3x - 5 = 0$
2. a) $y = 2x + 1$　　　　　b) $y = 7x - 2$
   c) $y = -6x - 4$　　　　d) $y = -\frac{7}{2}x - 1$
3. -1.56,　2.56;　$x^2 - x - 4 = 0$
4. -2.62,　7.62;　$x^2 - 5x - 20 = 0$
5. ± 3.46;　$x^2 + 2x - 5 = 0$;　-3.45,　1.45
6. From -3.74 to 1.07;　$3x^2 + 8x - 12 = 0$
7. From -1.74 to 5.74;　$x^2 - 4x - 10 = 0$

8. -0.39, 3.89; from 0.44 to 4.56; 0.44, 4.56; $8x^2 - 33x - 16 = 0$

9. $y = \frac{1}{2}x + 6$; -2.71, -2.21 } These are calculated values. This

10. $y = 2 - 5x$; -5.37 and 0.37 } accuracy is not attainable from a sketch.

11. $15, 0, 3$; $0.68, 3.32$; $4x^2 - 16x + 9 = 0$; from 0.40 to 3.10;
     $0.40, 3.10$; $4x^2 - 14x + 5 = 0$

EXERCISE 5d   It is worth pointing out that the local maximum or minimum does not neces-
sarily occur at one of the points given in the table.

1. a) 2.71   b) –2.47
2. a) 3.68   b) 3.42
3. a) -3.1 b) 3.1
4. -3
5. 1.75
6. a) $y = x$ b) –1, 0, 1

EXERCISE 5e   Discuss the problem that arises as the value of x gets close to zero. Hence
justify the range of values of x given in each question.

1. One   a) 0.77   b) -0.63
2. a) 2.61   b) $x > 2.14$ c) Lowest value is 1 when $x = 12$
3. a) 1.5,   10.5   b) $x^2 - 12x + 16 = 0$ c) From 1.5 to 10.5
4. a) -4
     b) $x^2 + 2x - 8 = 0$; two; draw the graph of $y = \frac{8}{x}$ for values of x from 1 to 8
5. a) y gets smaller and smaller   b) No   c) No
6. From 0.65 to 4.60, $4x^2 - 21x + 12 = 0$
7. a) $y = x + 1$ b) No. There is a negative solution

EXERCISE 5f   **1. D**   **2. B**   **3. A**   **4. C**   **5. B**   **6. A**

By the end of this chapter pupils should have a good idea of the shape of a
parabola, cubic curve and hyperbola and be able to recognise the forms of
equation that give rise to these curves. Encourage shape recognition by
asking them to sketch, without axes, the curves of a variety of these
equations.

CHAPTER 6   Indices

EXERCISE 6a   Revises earlier work but with more algebraic examples

1. 81	**6.** $\frac{49}{25}$	**11.** 1	**16.** 27
2. 16	**7.** $\frac{1}{2}$	**12.** $1\frac{1}{3}$	**17.** 25
3. 144	**8.** 6	**13.** 4	**18.** $\frac{9}{16}$
4. 64	**9.** 4	**14.** 27	**19.** $6\frac{1}{4}$
5. 144	**10.** 1	**15.** 32	**20.** $\frac{8}{27}$

21. 1	**26.** c^2	**31.** b^4	**36.** $\frac{1}{p^2}$
22. $\frac{27}{125}$	**27.** c^2	**32.** y^2	**37.** 81
23. $\frac{5}{2}$	**28.** $\frac{1}{x^4}$	**33.** x^2	**38.** 64
24. 64	**29.** b^7	**34.** $\frac{4}{d^2}$	**39.** 15 625
25. b^5	**30.** $\frac{b}{a}$	**35.** $\frac{1}{x^3}$	**40.** x^8

41. a^{10}	**46.** x^{15}	**51.** $\frac{2}{x^2}$	**56.** $15y^3$
42. x^6	**47.** y^8	**52.** $18x^3$	**57.** $\frac{4}{a^2}$
43. 512	**48.** x^{-6}	**53.** $2x$	**58.** $12x^5$
44. 729	**49.** $16a^5$	**54.** $\frac{1}{2a}$	**59.** $24y^4$
45. 256	**50.** $4p$	**55.** $4x^4$	**60.** $\frac{5}{y^2}$

EXERCISE 6b   When revising standard form remind pupils about scientific notation on calculators and how to 'read' the display.

1. 2.8×10^2	**4.** 9.7×10^{-2}	**7.** 8×10^{-1}
2. 3.9×10^{-1}	**5.** 2.77×10^3	**8.** 8×10^3
3. 7.07×10^2	**6.** 8×10^{-5}	**9.** 2.05×10^{-2}

10. 8.4×10^5	**13.** 1.15×10^{-5}	**16.** 2×10^3
11. 1.08×10^{10}	**14.** 3.2×10^2	**17.** 7×10^4
12. 1.54×10^{-4}	**15.** 7.8×10^{-2}	**18.** 3×10^{-2}

19. 1.4×10^{-5} **22.** 3.2×10^{3} **25.** 4.13×10^{-3}
20. 3×10^{0} **23.** 3.2×10^{-2} **26.** 2.59×10^{-2}
21. 1.25×10^{8} **24.** 3.31×10^{5} **27.** 2.8×10^{6}

28. a) 6×10^{3} b) 2.4×10^{6} c) 1.2005×10^{5}
29. a) 8.64×10^{-12} b) 6×10^{-2} c) 1.128×10^{-5}
30. a) 1.3×10^{3} b) 5.2×10^{7} c) 2.6005×10^{3} d) 2.5995×10^{4}

EXERCISE 6c   Emphasise, repeatedly, that $\sqrt{4}, 4^{\frac{1}{2}}, \ldots$ mean the positive root. If the negative root is required we write $-\sqrt{4}, -4^{\frac{1}{2}}$ and if both are required, $\pm\sqrt{4}, \pm 4^{\frac{1}{2}}$.

1. 3   **4.** 2   **7.** $\frac{1}{2}$ **10.** $\frac{2}{3}$
2. 4   **5.** 5   **8.** 0.2   **11.** 0.5
3. 6   **6.** 4   **9.** $\frac{1}{2}$ **12.** $\frac{2}{3}$

EXERCISE 6d   **1.** 9   **9.** 4   **17.** $\frac{1}{4}$ **25.** $x^{\frac{1}{2}}$

2. $\frac{1}{4}$ **10.** 100   **18.** $\frac{1}{8}$ **26.** x^{2}

3. 8   **11.** 0.001   **19.** $\frac{1}{2}$ **27.** y^{2}

4. 25   **12.** 100   **20.** 1000   **28.** a^{2}

5. 0.04   **13.** 3   **21.** 0.01   **29.** x^{6}

6. 1728   **14.** $3\frac{1}{2}$ **22.** 27   **30.** x^{4}

7. 0.216   **15.** 5   **23.** $11\frac{1}{9}$

8. 27   **16.** $1\frac{1}{2}$ **24.** 0.4

EXERCISE 6e   **1.** 2.88   **4.** 2.93   **7.** 7.95   **10.** 1.08
2. 4.90   **5.** 0.215   **8.** 2.45   **11.** 0.681
3. 3.16   **6.** 1.48   **9.** 0.381   **12.** 2.22

EXERCISE 6f   **1.** C   **2.** B   **3.** D   **4.** B   **5.** D   **6.** C   **7.** A

EXERCISE 6g   **1.** a) 4   b) $\frac{1}{7}$ c) 16   d) 125

2. a) $\frac{1}{4}$ b) 3   c) 1   d) $\frac{27}{16}$

3. a) $\frac{1}{16}$ b) 1   c) $\frac{2}{5}$ d) $12\frac{1}{2}$

4. a) 8.1×10^6 **b)** 2.73×10^4 **c)** 9×10

5. a) $\dfrac{1}{x}$ **b)** $\dfrac{2}{a^2}$ **c)** $\dfrac{y}{x^2}$

6. a) 2   **b)** 4

EXERCISE 6h   **1. a)** $\dfrac{9}{16}$ **b)** $1\dfrac{2}{3}$ **c)** 2   **d)** 1

2. a) 4.32×10^{-5} **b)** 7.5×10^{-2} **c)** 2.58×10^{-2} **d)** 2.22×10^{-2}

3. a) 5   **b)** $\dfrac{1}{36}$ **c)** $\dfrac{1}{125}$ **d)** $\dfrac{6}{25}$

4. a) $2\dfrac{1}{4}$ **b)** $\dfrac{9}{25}$ **c)** $2\dfrac{1}{2}$ **d)** $1\dfrac{19}{81}$

5. a) p^2 **b)** $\dfrac{1}{2x}$ **c)** x^{12}

6. a) 3   **b)** 3

EXERCISE 6i   **1. a)** $\dfrac{16}{81}$ **b)** $\dfrac{2}{3}$ **c)** $5\dfrac{4}{9}$ **d)** 8

2. a) 64   **b)** 25   **c)** 4   **d)** 8

3. a) x^2 **b)** $\dfrac{3}{2y^3}$ **c)** y^8

4. a) 6.4×10^9 **b)** 1.6×10 **c)** 6.25×10^{-2} **d)** 3×10^5

5. a) p^{10} **b)** $x^{\frac{3}{2}}$ **c)** $\dfrac{2}{5y}$

6. a) $\pm\dfrac{2}{3}$ **b)** $\dfrac{1}{3}$

CHAPTER 7   Cylinders, Cones and Spheres

The Value of π

The approximate value of π given by a scientific calculator is used in this chapter. If by any chance this value is not available then 3.142 may be used. Some examination papers specify the approximate value to be used so some practice in using 3.142 or $\dfrac{22}{7}$ may be needed.

Encourage estimation of answers: for this purpose use $\pi \approx 3$.

EXERCISE 7a

1. 56.5 cm,   254 cm²
2. 20.1 cm,   32.2 cm²
3. 151 m,   1810 m²
4. 146 mm,   1660 mm²
5. 81.7 cm,   531 cm²
6. 12.6 cm,   12.6 cm²
7. 6.66 cm,   3.53 cm²
8. 89.2 mm,   633 mm²
9. 18.2 cm,   26.4 cm²
10. 45.9 cm,   167 cm²
11. 5.65 m,   2.54 m²
12. 120 mm,   1150 mm²
13. 55.3 cm,   243 cm²
14. 647 mm,   333 cm²
15. 7.54 m,   4.52 m²
16. 119 cm,   1130 cm²
17. 256 cm,   5200 cm²
18. 584 mm,   272 cm²
19. 6π cm, 9π cm²
20. 24π cm, 144π cm²
21. 160π cm, 6400π cm²
22. 2π m, π m²
23. 9π m, 20.25π m²
24. 22π mm, 121π mm²

25. 207 cm
26. 6080 cm²
27. 49.7 cm²
28. 92.5 cm,   509 cm²
29. 201 cm²

30. a) 244 m   b) 213 m   c) 1140 m²
31. 56π cm²   **32. D**   **33. C**

EXERCISE 7b

1. 2.90 cm
2. 10.8 cm
3. 2.23 cm
4. 0.414 cm
5. 4.77 m
6. 30.6 m
7. 0.668 m
8. 17.2 cm
9. 2.07 mm

10. 23.6 mm
11. 15.8 cm
12. 7 cm
13. 0.54 m
14. 10.0 mm
15. 38 mm
16. 37.6 mm
17. 1.10 m
18. 45 cm

19. 3.66 cm
20. 6.15 m
21. 2.88 mm
22. 1.13 m
23. 6.28 cm
24. 4.22 cm
25. 1.69 cm
26. 19.5 mm
27. 2.03 m

28. 35.0 mm,   3850 mm²
29. 15.9 cm,   796 cm²
30. 3.12 cm
31. 4.44 cm,   27.9 cm²
32. 3.09 cm

EXERCISE 7c   Some examples for discussion, are needed:
e.g.

If arc AB is $\frac{1}{3}$ of the circumference, what is the size of angle x?

What fraction of the area of the circle is the area of the sector?

1. 10.5 cm,   52.4 m²   **3.** 1.88 cm,   2.26 cm²   **5.** 188 m,   6790 m²
2. 10.5 cm,   26.2 m²   **4.** 4.19 cm,   6.70 cm²   **6.** 3.14 m,   18.8 m²

7. 35.7 cm,   78.5 cm²   **8.** 85.7 cm,   370 cm²   **9.** 12.8 cm, 9.24 cm²

10. 66.8 °   **12.** 15.3 °   **14.** 8.91 cm
11. 43.0 °   **13.** 8.59 cm   **15.** 3.44 m

16. a) 36 °   b) 86 cm²
17. a) 12.6 cm   c) 120 °   d) 37.7 cm²   e) 37.7 cm²
18. a) 8 cm²   b) 4.57 cm²
19. a) 495 m²   b) 106 m²

EXERCISE 7d   **1.** 44 cm,   154 cm²   **3.** 110 cm, $962\frac{1}{2}$ cm² **5.** 4.4 cm,   1.54 cm²
          2. 11 cm, $9\frac{5}{8}$ cm²   **4.** 440 cm, 15 400 cm² **6.** $14\frac{2}{3}$ cm, $18\frac{2}{9}$ cm²

          7. 18 cm   **8.** $38\frac{1}{2}$ cm²   **9.** 22 m   **10.** 154 cm²

          11. 7 cm   **13.** $1\frac{3}{4}$ cm   **15.** $1\frac{2}{5}$ m
          12. 28 cm   **14.** $5\frac{1}{4}$ cm   **16.** 70 cm

EXERCISE 7e   **1.** 151 cm²   **5.** 1210 cm² or 0.121 m²
          2. 377 cm²   **6.** 255 cm²
          3. 226 cm²   **7.** 13 700 cm²
          4. 103 000 cm² or 10.3 m² **8.** 259 m²

          9. a) 377 cm²   b) 113 cm²   c) 603 cm²   **11.** 209 cm²
          10. a) 96.5 cm²   b) 161 cm²   **12.** 928 cm²

          13. 4.40 m²

EXERCISE 7f   **1.** 430 cm³   **5.** 1320 cm³
          2. 257 cm³   **6.** 34 500 cm³
          3. 21.2 m³   **7.** 74 000 cm³ or 0.074 m³
          4. 1020 mm³   **8.** 3.08 m³

          9. a) 61 100 cm³   b) 61.1 litres
          10. a) 43.2 cm³   b) 834 g
          11. a) 10 053 cm²   b) 20 holes

          12. 2.38 cm   **14.** 1.73 cm   **16.** 16.8 cm
          13. 2.69 cm   **15.** 2.11 m   **17.** 1.22 cm

18. 1.27 m   **21.** 54.0 cm
19. a) 1 m³   b) 1.03 m   **22.** 707 cm³
20. 20 cm

EXERCISE 7g   **1.** 1700 cm³   **5.** 27.2 cm³   **8.** 330 cm³
                   2. 29.4 cm³   **6.** 0.427 m³   **9.** 228 cm³
                   3. 78 200 cm³   **7.** 1150 cm³   **10.** 113 cm³
                   4. 0.528 cm³

EXERCISE 7h   The most able pupils may be interested in the derivation of the formula
                   $A = \pi r l$.

  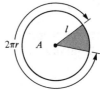

Considering the cone made from a sector of a circle then:

$$\frac{A}{\pi l^2} = \frac{2\pi r}{2\pi l} \Rightarrow A = \pi r l$$

1. 126 cm²   **4.** 15 200 mm²   **6.** a) 302 cm³
2. 434 cm²   **5.** 163 cm²   b) 10 cm
3. 4.15 cm²   c) 188 cm²

EXERCISE 7i   Tell the pupils that the formulae for the volume and curved surface area of a
                   sphere cannot be proved at this stage.

                   1. 113 cm³   **5.** 24.4 m³   **8.** a) 145 cm³
                   2. 1560 cm³   **6.** 9200 mm³   b) 4.52 cm
                   3. 230 000 cm³   **7.** 262 cm³
                   4. 0.998 cm³   **9.** $\frac{9}{2}\pi$ cm³

EXERCISE 7j   **1.** 1020 cm²   **3.** 21 100 cm²   **5.** 3320 cm²
                   2. 254 cm²   **4.** 10.2 cm²   **6.** (146 m²)   6 pots

EXERCISE 7k   **1.** 596   **5.** Sphere; 25.7 cm³

                   2. 572 cm²   **6.** a) $\frac{64}{3}\pi$ cm³   b) 64π cm³   c) $\frac{128}{3}\pi$ cm³

                   3. a) 15 cm   b) 3020 cm³   **7.** a) $\frac{32}{3}\pi$ cm³   b) $\frac{2048}{3}\pi$ cm³   c) 64

                   4. 239 000 cm³

EXERCISE 7l

1. Sphere; 16.5 cm^2
2. 462 cm^2
3. a) 15 cm   b) 679 cm^2
4. Total surface area = 32.4 m^2
   No
   Enough to cover 2.4 m^2 is still needed
5. 511 cm^2

EXERCISE 7m

1. C	3. A	5. D	7. B	9. C
2. B	4. D	6. A	8. D	10. B

CHAPTER 8   Similar Shapes

EXERCISE 8a   Revises earlier work on similar triangles.

1. Yes. The angles of the one triangle are equal to the angles of the other triangle
2. Yes. The three pairs of corresponding sides are in the same ratio
3. Yes. There is one pair of equal angles and the sides containing these equal angles are in the same ratio
4. Yes. $L\hat{M}N = Q\hat{P}R = 90°$ and the sides containing these angles are in the same ratio
5. Yes. The angles of $\triangle RST$ are equal to the angles of $\triangle ABC$
6. Yes. The three pairs of corresponding sides are in the same ratio
7. Yes. $B\hat{A}C = Q\hat{R}P = 85°$ and the sides containing these angles are in the same ratio
8. Yes. The angles of $\triangle ABC$ are equal to the angles of $\triangle DEF$
9. a) Each triangle contains a right angle and the sides containing the right angles are in the same ratio
   b) The value of each is $\frac{1}{2}$
10. Yes, $\frac{PR}{QR} = \frac{1}{2}$, $PR = 2\frac{1}{2}$ cm
11. $\frac{1}{2}$,   6 mm
12. The three angles of $\triangle ABC$ are equal to the three angles of $\triangle APQ$
13. Yes

EXERCISE 8b   Nos 11 to 14 introduce the intercept theorem.

3. Yes, Yes   4. 60°   6. No   7. 5 m   9. 6 m

11. b) $QC = 3\frac{3}{4}$ cm   c) $BQ = 2\frac{1}{4}$ cm   d) 3 : 5

12. b) XL = 2.4 cm   c) MZ = 6 cm   d) 2 : 3
13. b) AD = 4 cm   c) 4 : 1
14. b) AY = 10 cm   c) 1 : 2

EXERCISE 8c   **1.** 3 cm   **3.** $2\frac{2}{3}$ cm   **5.** 3 cm   **7.** 7.5 cm   **9.** 8 cm

                 2. $2\frac{2}{3}$ cm   **4.** 6 cm   **6.** 2.4 cm   **8.** 1 cm   **10.** 2 cm

EXERCISE 8d   Inaccuracies frequently arise in drawing lines of a particular length. Pupils should be reminded that it is necessary to move the eye so that the eye, the mark on the ruler, and the mark on the paper are always in the same straight line. Stress the importance of a suitably sharpened pencil together with a correct handling of compasses and other instruments.

5. a) 2x, 3x, 4x, 5x
    b) 1 : 4,   2 : 3,   3 : 2,   4 : 1
9. 7

EXERCISE 8e   Questions 1 to 3 are suitable for class discussion.

1. a) 1 : 2 : 3 : 4
    b) 1 : 4 : 9 : 16
    c) Yes. Numbers in (b) are the squares of those in (a)

2. a) 1 : 2 : 3 : 4
    b) 1 : 4 : 9 : 16
    c) As for No.1

3. a) 1 : 2 : 3 : 4
    b) 1 : 4 : 9 : 16
    c) As for No.1

4. a) PR = 20 cm   b) QS = 12 cm
    c) $\triangle$ABC = 30 cm², $\triangle$PQR = 120 cm²
    d) 1 : 4

5. XW = 2 cm, $\triangle$ABC = 9 cm², $\triangle$XYZ = 4 cm²
6. LN = 8 cm, $\triangle$ABC = 25 cm², $\triangle$LMN = 16 cm²
7. BC = 9 cm,   Area ABCD = 27 cm²,   Area PQRS = 3 cm²
8. LP = 3 cm,   Area WXYZ = 32 cm²,   Area LMNP = 18 cm²

9.

Similar figures	Ratio of sides	Ratio areas
Triangles in question 5	3 : 2	9 : 4
Triangles in question 6	5 : 4	25 : 16
Rectangles in question 7	3 : 1	9 : 1
Parallelograms in question 8	4 : 3	16 : 9

EXERCISE 8f **1.** $4:1$ **7.** $1:1225$ **13.** $5:4$
            2. $9:25$ **8.** $1:400$ **14.** $7:4$
            3. $4:9$ **9.** $1:36$ **15.** $5:8$
            4. $9:16$ **10.** $5:3$ **16.** 8 cm^2
            5. $25:9$ **11.** $3:2$ **17.** 16 cm^2
            6. $16:25$ **12.** $2:1$ **18.** 7.5 cm^2

19. 64 cm^2 **20.** $6:5$ **21.** 2.1 cm   **22.** 50 cm^2

EXERCISE 8g **1.** $1\frac{1}{2}$ cm^2 **2.** $2:1$ **3.** 200 m^2 **4.** $4:1$

5. a) 2.25 cm   b) $\frac{9}{49}$ c) $\frac{9}{40}$

6. $4:9$, $2:3$
7. a) i) 9 cm   ii) 12 cm   iii) $\frac{1}{16}$ iv) $\frac{9}{16}$
    b) i) $16a$ ii) $3a$
8. AD $= 2$ cm

EXERCISE 8h A plentiful supply of cubes or cuboids would be most useful as an introduction to this exercise. Sets of similar containers, e.g. cylinders or jugs, may also help to demonstrate the point that is being made.

1. a) $1:2:3$ b) $1:2:3$ c) $1:8:27$
2. a) i) $2:3$ ii) $2:3$ iii) $2:3$
    b) $8:27$
3. a) $3:2:5$ b) $27:8:125$
4. a) i) $1:2:5$ ii) $1:2:5$
    b) $1:8:125$

EXERCISE 8i Much may be made of the practical nature of much of this exercise.

1. $8:1$ **2.** $27:64$ **3.** $2:3$

4. a) $4:3$ b) $4:3$
5. a) $4:1$ b) $8:1$
6. a) $1:100$ b) $1:1000$ c) $1:10$ d) $1:1$
7. $1\frac{11}{16}$ pts, 4 pts
8. $4\frac{1}{2}$ p
9. 125 centilitres, 216 centilitres
10. a) 9 cm , 12 cm   b) 64 cm^2, 100 cm^2
11. a) $1:50$ b) $1:125\,000$ c) 3 cm   d) 7500 cm^2 or 0.75 m^2

12. 64 kg
13. a) 12 : 13   b) 1728 : 2197
14. a) 21%   b) 33%
15. a) 224%   b) 483%
16. a) 44%   b) 73%
17. a) 26%   b) 59%
18. 36%

EXERCISE 8j

2. 7 : 5
3. b) i) QZ = 20 cm   ii) XQ = 10 cm   c) 1 : 2,   2 : 3
5. a) 3 cm   b) 5 : 3   c) 3 : 5

EXERCISE 8k

1. a) 7 : 9   b) 7 : 9
2. a) 45 cm^2 b) 4 : 9   c) 3 : 4
3. a) 3.2 cm   b) 4 : 9   c) $\frac{16}{81}$

d) $\frac{16}{65}$ e) $\frac{4}{5}$ f) $\frac{4}{9}$

4. a) $\frac{1}{3}$ b) $\frac{1}{3}$ c) $\frac{2}{3}$

d) $\frac{2}{3}$ e) $\frac{1}{9}$ f) $\frac{4}{9}$

5. $\frac{1}{8}$

CHAPTER 9   Information Matrices

EXERCISE 9a

1. a) $\begin{pmatrix} 100 & 300 & \boxed{50} \\ \boxed{200} & 0 & 300 \end{pmatrix}$
   b)
   c) 300

2. a) and b) $\begin{pmatrix} \boxed{50} & 25 & 37 \\ 100 & 150 & 89 \\ 92 & \boxed{250} & 340 \end{pmatrix}$
   c) 339

3. a) and b) $\begin{pmatrix} 200 & 150 & 120 \\ 350 & 200 & 70 \\ 190 & \boxed{250} & 100 \\ 280 & 210 & 110 \end{pmatrix}$ 4 × 3
   c) 400   d) 620

e) $\begin{pmatrix} 200 & 350 & 190 & 280 \\ 150 & 200 & 250 & \underline{210} \\ 120 & 70 & 100 & 110 \end{pmatrix}$

4. a) cost (p) potatoes carrots parsnips

$$\mathbf{M} = \begin{array}{c} A \\ B \end{array}\begin{pmatrix} 10 & 8 & 12 \\ 12 & ⑨ & 10 \end{pmatrix}$$

c)   lb

$$\mathbf{P} = \begin{pmatrix} 5 \\ 1 \\ 2 \end{pmatrix} \begin{array}{l} \text{potatoes} \\ \text{carrots} \\ \text{parsnips} \end{array}$$

d) 82 p

e) $\begin{pmatrix} 82 \\ 89 \end{pmatrix}$

f) Top entry gives the cost of Mr Smith's purchase in shop A
Bottom entry gives the cost of Mr Smith's purchase in shop B

5. a) 21 500
b) 15 000

$$\begin{array}{cccc} & A & B & C \\ c) \ \mathbf{N} = (& 20 & 50 & 100 \ ) \end{array}$$

d) The top and bottom entries in **NM** give the answers to (a) and (b)

6. a) 80

b) $\begin{pmatrix} 80 \\ 180 \end{pmatrix}$; gives the number of coins on each emptying

c) 1700 p

d) $\begin{pmatrix} 10 \\ 20 \\ 50 \end{pmatrix}$

e) The entries in **AV** give the amounts (in pence) of money

EXERCISE 9b   Question 8 is demanding. It involves route matrices. The most able will enjoy puzzling this one out themselves but use it for discussion with other pupils.

1. $\mathbf{NM} = (18 \quad 9 \quad 10)$ and lists the total number of matches won, drawn and lost

$\mathbf{MP} = \begin{pmatrix} 13 \\ 11 \\ 13 \end{pmatrix}$ and lists the number of matches played by each team

$\mathbf{M} \begin{pmatrix} 2 \\ 1 \\ 0 \end{pmatrix} = \begin{pmatrix} 18 \\ 14 \\ 13 \end{pmatrix}$ and lists the points accumulated by each team

2. a)
$$\mathbf{TC} = \begin{pmatrix} \pounds \\ 223 \\ 279 \\ 310 \end{pmatrix}$$ and lists cost of raw materials each month

b)
$$\mathbf{TR} = \begin{pmatrix} \text{hrs} \\ 90 \\ 85 \\ 110 \end{pmatrix}$$ and lists the time taken to make each month's orders

$$\mathbf{TC} + 10\mathbf{TR} = \begin{pmatrix} \pounds \\ 1123 \\ 1129 \\ 1410 \end{pmatrix}$$ and lists the total cost of each month's orders

3. a) $(7 \quad 10 \quad 39)$; lists the numbers of each type of milk ordered

b) $\begin{pmatrix} 21 \\ 20 \\ 15 \end{pmatrix}$; lists the number of bottles ordered by each customer

c) $\begin{pmatrix} 532 \\ 500 \\ 395 \end{pmatrix}$; cost (p) to each customer for the week

d) (1427); cost (p) of milk sold in the flats that week

4. a) $\begin{pmatrix} 17 \\ 16 \\ 32 \end{pmatrix}$; number of employees in each factory

b) $(33 \quad 18 \quad 14)$; number of employees in each category

c) $\begin{pmatrix} 1580 \\ 1420 \\ 2700 \end{pmatrix}$; the weekly wage bill for each factory

d) (5700); the total weekly wage bill for the three factories

5. a) (107000); total daily calorie requirements of all the people in the hostel

b) (85); the number of people in the hostel

6. a) $\begin{array}{c} \\ A \\ B \end{array} \begin{pmatrix} \text{I} & \text{II} & \text{III} & \text{IV} \\ 2100 & 2300 & 2300 & 1400 \\ 1950 & 2340 & 2250 & 1560 \end{pmatrix}$; cost of items ordered each quarter from source A and from source B

b) $\begin{pmatrix} 8100 \\ 8100 \end{pmatrix}$

c) B
d) both the same

7. $\begin{pmatrix} 128 & 106 & 34 \\ 105 & 87 & 28 \\ 174 & 144 & 46 \end{pmatrix}$; the figures ringed show the week's pay of each employee

(261); the total weeks pay of the three employees

8. $\begin{array}{cccc} \text{C} & \text{D} & \text{E} & \text{F} \\ \end{array}$
$\begin{pmatrix} 1 & 0 & 1 & 0 \\ 1 & 1 & 0 & 1 \\ 2 & 1 & 1 & 1 \end{pmatrix} \begin{array}{c} \text{X} \\ \text{Y} \\ \text{Z} \end{array}$

The entries show the number of train routes available between C, D, E, F and X, Y, Z

EXERCISE 9c   Questions 4 and 5 involve route matrices and they are both *extremely* demanding. Pupils, other than the most able, should not try these without help.

1. $(5 \quad 1 \quad 1.5)$; $(5 \quad 1 \quad 1.5)\mathbf{R}\begin{pmatrix} 1 \\ 1 \\ 1 \end{pmatrix}$

2.

$$S\begin{pmatrix}1\\1\\1\\1\end{pmatrix}; \quad \begin{matrix}A\\B\end{matrix}\begin{pmatrix}40 & 30 & 25\\35 & 30 & 29\end{pmatrix}S$$

3. a)

$$F\begin{pmatrix}1\\1\\1\end{pmatrix}$$

b)

$$F\begin{pmatrix}25\\28\\30\end{pmatrix}$$

c) $(1\ 1\ 1)\ F$

d) $(1\ \ 1\ \ 1)\ F\begin{pmatrix}25\\28\\30\end{pmatrix}$

4. a) The top row shows the number of direct services available *from* X to X, Y and A. Similarly for the other rows
The first column shows the number of direct services *to* X from X, Y and A. Similarly the other columns

b)

$$R^2 = \begin{matrix}X\\Y\\A\end{matrix}\begin{matrix}X & Y & A\\ \begin{pmatrix}9 & 1 & 0\\0 & 9 & 3\\3 & 0 & 0\end{pmatrix}\end{matrix}$$

The entries in the main diagonal show the number of ways it is possible to travel from one place to another and then back again without a break in either journey

5. a) $FA = \begin{pmatrix}1 & 1 & 0\\1 & 2 & 1\end{pmatrix}$

b) $BF = \begin{pmatrix}1 & 0\\1 & 1\\2 & 1\end{pmatrix}$

c)

$$BFA = \begin{matrix}X\\Y\\Z\end{matrix}\begin{matrix}L & M & N\\ \begin{pmatrix}1 & 1 & 0\\1 & 2 & 1\\2 & 3 & 1\end{pmatrix}\end{matrix}$$

The numbers 2 and 3 indicate that there are 2 and 3 air routes respectively between the towns indicated by the positions of the entries

CHAPTER 10   Geometric Proof

This chapter attempts to show how to give a reasoned argument and why this is desirable. The examples in the exercises are not numerical, but reasoned solutions to numerical problems are expected at this level and should be insisted upon. Most pupils doing the higher level GCSE appreciate the need for a theoretical proof and many will be stimulated by a discussion on Euclidean Geometry and its structure. This gives the pupils an insight into mathematics as an academic subject in its own right as opposed to its use as a tool for other subjects.

Pupils, other than the most able, may find the exercises, as given in this chapter, difficult. In this case change them to numerical questions; for example when a relationship between angles has to be proved, give a size for one angle and ask for the size of the other angle.

EXERCISE 10a It is worth developing number 6 to show how all the other circle angle facts can be deduced from this proof.

CHAPTER 11 Circles and Tangents

If Chapter 10 has not been covered, a revision of all the geometry contained in that chapter is desirable.

EXERCISE 11a **1.** A straight line parallel to the ground, 20 cm above it.
     a) one   b) 20 cm   c) radius, $90°$

2. 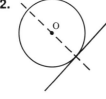 **3.**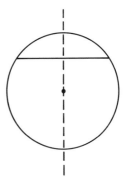

4. b) A tangent, touching the circle at N. $90°$

EXERCISE 11b Use at least one question for discussion, emphasising the need for a rough sketch before embarking on the actual construction. Also remind the pupils of the need for a *sharp* pencil.

    1. OB = 5 cm, CB = 2 cm   **3.** $x = 50°$, $y = 40°$
    2. $30°$ **4.** $x = 20°$, $y = 70°$

5. $x = 40°$, $y = 50°$ **8.** 30°

6. AB = 12 cm, $\stackrel{\wedge}{\text{OB}}\text{A} = 22.6°$ **9.** 5 cm

7. $x = 30°$, $y = 60°$, $z = 60°$ **11.** 9.80 cm (correct to 3 s.f.)

EXERCISE 11c   **2.** $\stackrel{\wedge}{\text{CA}}\text{P} = 90°$. PA and PB are tangents to the circle centre C

4. a) 4 cm

EXERCISE 11d   With the less able use only for discussion.

EXERCISE 11e   **1.** $p = 65°$, $q = 65°$
2. $e = f = 67°$, $i = g = 23°$, $h = 134°$
3. a) 50°   b) a kite (also a cyclic quadrilateral)
4. $x = 96°$, $y = 48°$
5. $r = 36°$, $s = 36°$
6. a) 6 cm   b) 73.7° (to 1 d.p.)
7. 8 cm
8. Yes
9. 5.77 cm (to 3 s.f.)
10. 60°, 8 cm, 13.9 cm (to 3 s.f.)
11. 19.3 cm, 13.7 cm, 13.7 cm (to 3 s.f.)
13. They are equal

Alternate Segment Theorem
Demonstrations of this theorem should be given before the formal proof. If the demonstrations suggested in the answer book for 3A (page 39) were used, and the pieces of card are still available, it can be repeated. Also constructing and measuring is convincing:

e.g.
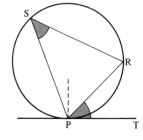

Construct a tangent to a circle (radius $\simeq$ 5 cm) and draw any chord, PR, then complete the figure using any point S on the circumference. Measure the shaded angles.

EXERCISE 11f   **1.** 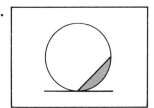   **3.**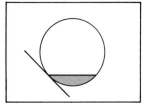

2. 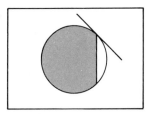   **4.**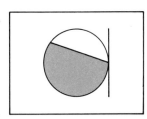

5. $d = 73°$, $e = 26°$, $f = 81°$
6. $p = q = r = s = 60°$
7. $k = m = l = 64°$, $n = 52°$
8. $u = v = 67°$
9. $q = 57°$, $p = 57°$
10. $w = 90°$, $x = 27°$, $y = 117°$
11. $d = e = f = 47°$, $g = 86°$
12. $e = f = g = 54°$, $h = 72°$
13. $k = 74°$, $l = m = 53°$
14. $r = 90°$, $t = 35°$, $s = 55°$
15. $f = g = h = 71°$, $i = 38°$
16. $d = 90°$, $e = f = g = 45°$, $h = 90°$
17. $s = 30°$, $t = 60°$, $u = 60°$, $v = 10°$
18. $x = 28°$, $y = 62°$, $z = 62°$
19. $i = k = l = 37°$, $j = 53°$
20. $x = 60°$, $y = 61.5°$, $z = 58.5°$

CHAPTER 12   Probability

EXERCISE 12a   This exercise revises simple probability but with harder examples. Some of the questions are very demanding.

1. a) $\frac{1}{3}$ b) $\frac{5}{9}$ c) 1   d) 0

2. a) $\frac{3}{10}$ b) $\frac{1}{5}$

3. a) $\frac{5}{26}$ b) $\frac{1}{2}$ c) $\frac{3}{13}$

4. a) $\frac{11}{18}$ b) 1

5. $\frac{5}{12}$ **8.** a) $\frac{3}{10}$ **9.** $\frac{1}{3}$ **12.** 16

6. $\frac{4}{7}$ b) $\frac{4}{5}$ **10.** 2   **13.** 28

7. $\frac{4}{15}$ c) $\frac{1}{5}$ **11.** 90

14. a) 0.503   b) 0.497

15. a) $\frac{31}{40}$ b) $\frac{3}{40}$ c) $\frac{3}{7}$

16. 12, 13, 15, 21, 23, 25, 31, 32, 35, 51, 52, 53; $\frac{1}{4}$

17. D   **18.** B   **19.** A   **20.** B

EXERCISE 12b   Revises possibility spaces

1. a) $\frac{5}{36}$ b) $\frac{2}{9}$ c) $\frac{1}{18}$

2. a) $\frac{1}{4}$ b) $\frac{3}{4}$ c) $\frac{1}{2}$

3. a) $\frac{5}{12}$ b) $\frac{2}{3}$ c) $\frac{11}{36}$

4. a) $\frac{1}{4}$ b) $\frac{1}{4}$ c) $\frac{1}{9}$

5. a) $\frac{1}{2}$ b) $\frac{1}{4}$ c) $\frac{3}{4}$

6. a) $\frac{1}{4}$ b) $\frac{3}{4}$

EXERCISE 12c   **1.** a) i) $\frac{5}{8}$ ii) $\frac{3}{8}$ b) $\frac{3}{7}$ c) $\frac{4}{7}$

2. a) i) $\frac{1}{13}$ ii) $\frac{1}{4}$ b) $\frac{4}{17}$ c) $\frac{4}{51}$

3. a) $\frac{4}{9}$ b) i) $\frac{3}{8}$ ii) $\frac{5}{8}$ c) i) $\frac{1}{2}$ ii) $\frac{1}{2}$

EXERCISE 12d   **1.** a) $\frac{4}{9}$ b) $\frac{1}{2}$ c) $\frac{1}{6}$ d) $\frac{5}{18}$

2. a) $\frac{2}{5}$ b) $\frac{1}{3}$ c) $\frac{1}{3}$

3. a) $\frac{3}{7}$ b) $\frac{1}{7}$ c) $\frac{2}{7}$ d) $\frac{2}{7}$ e) $\frac{2}{7}$ f) $\frac{4}{7}$

4. a) $\frac{3}{4}$ b) $\frac{9}{16}$

5. a) $\frac{2}{3}$ b) $\frac{5}{8}$ c) $\frac{1}{2}$ d) $\frac{5}{21}$

Probability trees

We can see that if two events *both* happen we *multiply* the probabilities and that if *either* one *or* the other happens we *add*.

Hence we *multiply* the probabilities when we follow a path along the branches of the probability tree and *add* the results of following several paths.

EXERCISE 12e   **1.** a) $\frac{15}{28}$ b) $\frac{13}{28}$

2. $\frac{8}{15}$

3. $\frac{5}{12}$

4. a) $\frac{1}{8}$ b) $\frac{3}{8}$

5. a) $\frac{1}{16}$ b) $\frac{1}{16}$ c) $\frac{1}{16}$

d) $\frac{1}{16}$ e) $\frac{1}{4}$

6. $\frac{9}{17}$

7. a) $\frac{1}{9}$ b) $\frac{7}{18}$

8. $\frac{7}{15}$

EXERCISE 12f   **1.** a) i) $\frac{27}{100}$ ii) $\frac{9}{100}$ iii) $\frac{1}{5}$ b) i) $\frac{9}{1000}$ ii) $\frac{43}{250}$

2. a) $\frac{1}{4}$ b) $\frac{1}{6}$ c) $\frac{1}{3}$

3. a) $\frac{1}{5}$ b) $\frac{24}{145}$ c) $\frac{506}{1015}$ d) $\frac{509}{1015}$

4. a) i) $\frac{1}{9}$ ii) $\frac{4}{45}$ b) i) $\frac{1}{18}$ ii) $\frac{7}{90}$

5. a) $\frac{4}{25}$ b) $\frac{1}{50}$ c) $\frac{1}{20}$ d) $\frac{8}{125}$ e) $\frac{1}{1000}$

6. a) $\frac{4}{9}$ b) Bob

CHAPTER 13   Loci and Constructions

EXERCISE 13a   Some questions in this exercise have more than one correct solution. Any reasonable locus should be accepted. Unless stated otherwise, it will always be assumed that a straight line extends to infinity in both directions.

1. A complete circle

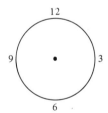

2. One twelfth of a circle

3. An arc from the bowler's hand to the wicket

4. A straight line
(assuming the ground is flat)

5. An arc

6. a) A straight line parallel to the road at a distance equal to the radius of the wheel from it

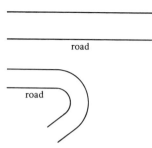

b) An arc at a constant distance from the curve forming the bend

7. A semicircle

8. Approximately a circle

9. A circle (approximately)

10. A spiral

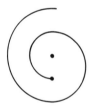

11. a) A circle of radius 80 cm
b) A semicircle of radius 80 cm
12. A straight line parallel to the top edge and 3 cm from it
13. Two straight lines parallel to AB and distant 3 cm from it
14. a) A circle, centre C, radius 4 cm
b) A circle, centre C, radius 8 cm
15. The line joining the midpoints of AD and BC
16. The perpendicular bisector of AB
17. The bisector of $A\hat{B}C$
18. a) The diagonal, BD, of the square
b) The diagonal, AC, of the square
    Yes. The centre of the square

19. A straight line parallel to AB and CD which is twice as far from AB as it is from CD.

20. a) A circle perpendicular to the plane of the paper with AB as diameter
b) A circle perpendicular to the plane of the paper with AD as diameter
c) A circle perpendicular to the plane of the paper with AC as diameter
d) A circle within the plane of the paper with OA as radius

EXERCISE 13b **1.** A circle, centre O, radius OM

2. The diameter of the circle which is perpendicular to AB

3. A straight line parallel to AB distant 6 cm from it

4. A circle on AB as diameter (This assumes that C can be on either side of AB)

5. A circle, centre A, radius 5 cm

6. The arc of the unique circle that passes through A, B and any position of C

7. A straight line parallel to OX, distant 2 cm from it on the same side as A

8. A circle, centre O, radius OT

9. a) A quadrant of a circle, centre A, radius AD

b) A quadrant of a circle, centre A, radius AC

10. a)

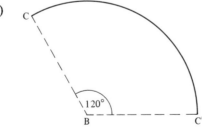

b)

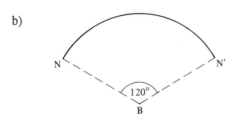

BA turns through 120°

11.

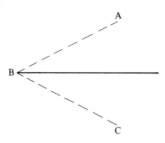

The locus is the bisector of $A\hat{B}C$

12.

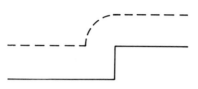

13. a) A circle of radius 4 cm, concentric with the circle of radius 5 cm
b) A circle of radius 6 cm, concentric with the circle of radius 5 cm

14. The perpendicular bisector of AB

15. It is the midpoint of AC

16.

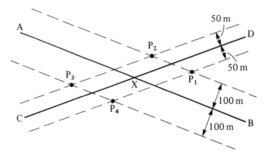

P_1, P_2, P_3, P_4 show the four possible positions for P

17.

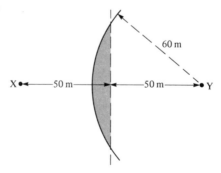

18.

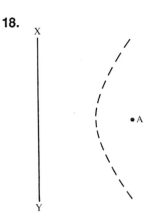

This curve is called a parabola

EXERCISE 13c Pupils should be reminded of the importance of neat and accurate constructions. In an ideal diagram the figure asked for, e.g. a quadrilateral, should stand out more strongly than any construction lines that have been used. Sketches should be encouraged for they enable the accurate construction to be well placed on the page and the correct method of construction chosen.

1.

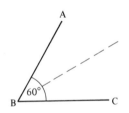

2.

3.

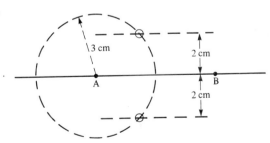

c) The loci intersect in **2** points. 6.1 cm

4.

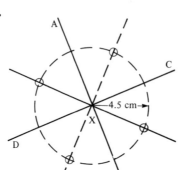

c) Four,   4.5 cm

5. The point is both equidistant from A and B, and from the lines AB and AC.

6.

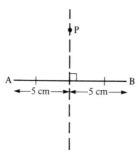

7.

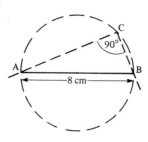

8.

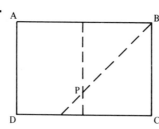

d) PC = 6.3 cm

9.

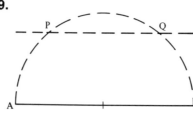

c) The difference between AP and PB is 4.9 cm

10.

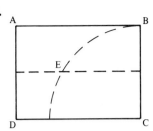

AE = 5.0 cm

11.

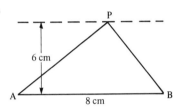

P could also be on the opposite side of AB

12.

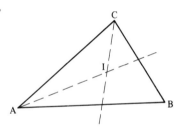

I is equidistant from the three sides AB, BC, CA

13.

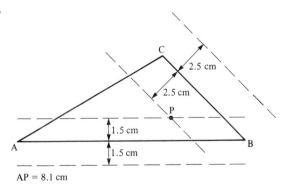

AP = 8.1 cm

14. PB = 4.5 cm   **16.** CD = 8.3 cm
15. DX = 4.2 cm   **17.** AD = 7.9 cm

EXERCISE 13d

1.

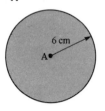

6 cm

A•

4.

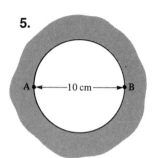

6 cm

3 cm

A   B

2.

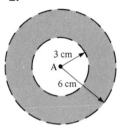

3 cm

A•

6 cm

5.

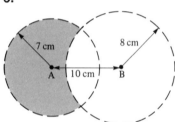

A •←10 cm→• B

3.

C

A   B

6.

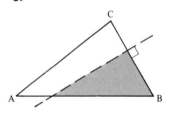

7 cm   8 cm

A   10 cm   B

7.

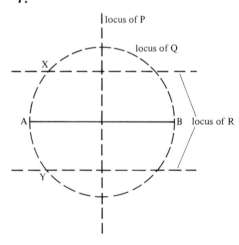

locus of P

locus of Q

X

A   B   locus of R

Y

AX = 2.1 cm
Y is a similar point

EXERCISE 13e   An exercise worth tackling whether it is in your examination syllabus or not.

1. A sphere, centre A, of radius 6 cm
2. The plane that bisects AB at right angles
3. a) A sphere, centre A, of radius 5 cm
   b) The plane that bisects AB at right angles
   c) A circle of radius 3 cm which lies in the plane that bisects AB at right angles
4. A sphere of radius 15 cm
5. Two circles, one of radius 5 cm and one of radius 15 cm. There are two possible circles in this case but only one in question 4
6. a) A circle, centre D, radius DA
   b) A circle, centre B, radius BA
   c) A circle, centre at N, the foot of the perpendicular from A to DB, radius AN
7. a) Two planes, one on each side of ABCD, each 8 cm from it
   b) The plane that bisects AD at right angles
   c) Two lines, on opposite sides of ABCD, parallel to AB and 8.9 cm ($\sqrt{80}$ cm) from both AB and DC
8. The circle of intersection of the plane which bisects AB at right angles and the sphere, centre C, radius 10 cm (this assumes that the loci intersect)
9. The line, perpendicular to ABC, that passes through the circumcentre of △ABC

CHAPTER 14   Transformations

Where scales are not given, 1 cm to 1 unit is the most convenient.

EXERCISE 14a   Revises the common transformations. Remind pupils about vectors with a few examples.

1.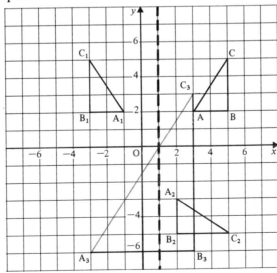

2.

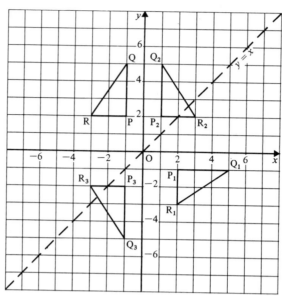

d) Rotation of 180° about O
e) Rotation of 90° anticlockwise about O

3.

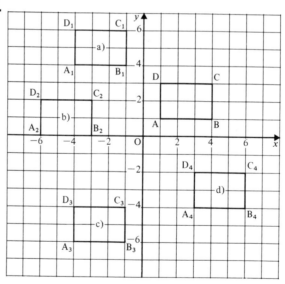

e) Translation defined by $\begin{pmatrix} -7 \\ 8 \end{pmatrix}$

f) Translation defined by $\begin{pmatrix} 7 \\ 1 \end{pmatrix}$

4.

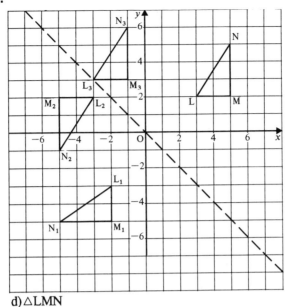

d) △LMN

5. a) Rotation of 90° clockwise about O

b) Reflection in the line $x = -1$

c) Translation defined by the vector $\begin{pmatrix} -8 \\ 6 \end{pmatrix}$

d) 90° anticlockwise

6. a) Translation defined by the vector $\begin{pmatrix} -6 \\ 0 \end{pmatrix}$

b) Rotation of 180° about O

c) Translation defined by the vector $\begin{pmatrix} -5 \\ -2 \end{pmatrix}$

d) Reflection in line $x = -2$

e) Translation defined by the vector $\begin{pmatrix} 8 \\ 0 \end{pmatrix}$

f) Reflection in line $x = 5$

g) Translation defined by the vector $\begin{pmatrix} 6 \\ 0 \end{pmatrix}$

h) Reflection in line $x = -2$

i) Rotation of 180° about (−3, 0)

7. a) $(5, 4)$ b) $(-1, 1)$ c) $(2, 0)$

8. a) $(2, 5)$ b) $(0, 1)$

9. a) Centre E, angle of rotation $90°$ clockwise
   b) Line EB
   c) Centre midpoint of EB, angle of rotation $180°$

10. a) $AB = BC = PB = BQ$, $AC = PQ$
   b) $60°$ clockwise   d) $105°$
   c) $60°$ clockwise, $60°$ e) 6 cm

11. a) $(2, -5)$; $90°$ anticlockwise
   b) Equidistant from A and A', B and B', C and C'

EXERCISE 14b   The notation introduced here is useful for discussing compound transformations. If the examination syllabus that you are following does not require compound transformations then omit this exercise together with 14c, 14d and 14e.

1.

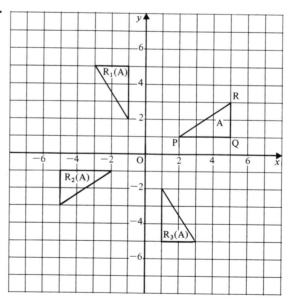

2.

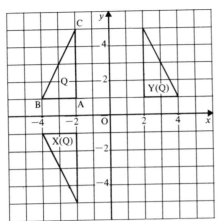

3.

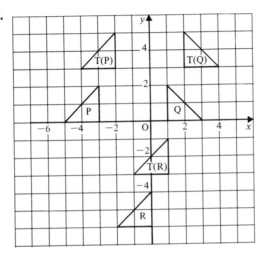

4.

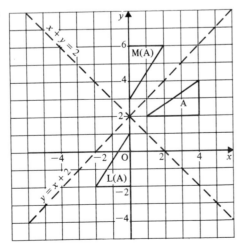

5.

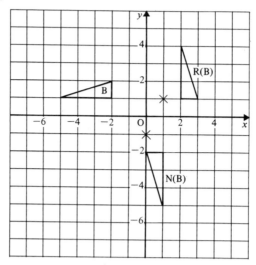

1.

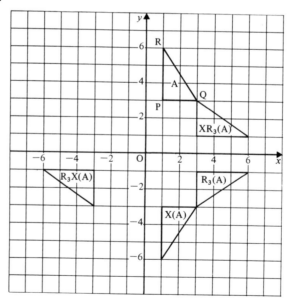

e) Reflection in line $y = -x$

2.

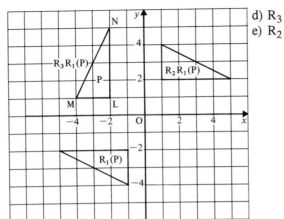

d) R_3
e) R_2

3.

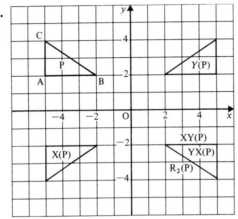

f) Yes   g) Yes
h) Rotation of $180°$
    about O, ie R_2

4.

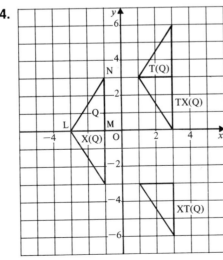

e) Translation defined by
   the vector $\begin{pmatrix} 4 \\ -3 \end{pmatrix}$

f) Translation defined by
   the vector $\begin{pmatrix} 0 \\ 6 \end{pmatrix}$

EXERCISE 14d **1.**

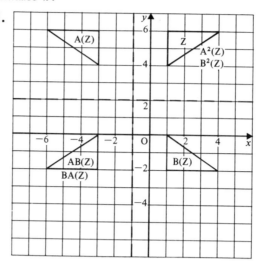

b) Rotation of 180°
   about O

   AB = BA

2.

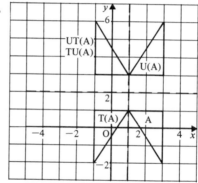

b) Yes
c) Yes

3.

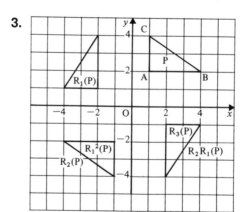

a) $R_1^2 = R_2$, $R_2 R_1 = R_3$

b) $R_3^2 = R_2$, $R_2 R_3 = R_1$, $R_3 R_2 = R_1$

EXERCISE 14 e **1.**

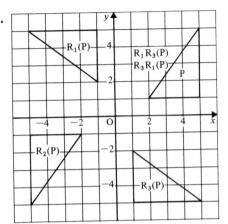

a) $R_1R_2 = R_3R_1 = I$
b) $R_2{}^2 = I \quad R_2R_3 = R_1$,
   $R_1R_2 = R_3$

2.

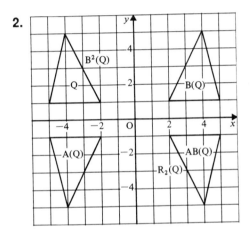

b) i) $B^2 = I$
   ii) $AB = R_2$

3.

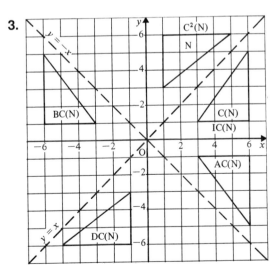

b) i) $DC = R_2$
   ii) $C^2 = I$
   iii) $AC = R_3$
   iv) $BC = R_1$
   v) $IC = C$

4.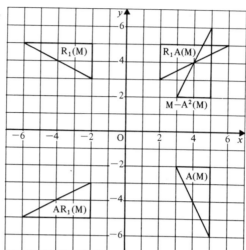

b) i) $A^2 = I$
   ii) $AR_1 = D$
   iii) $R_1 A = C$
c) False

5.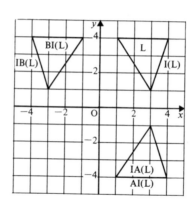

b) $AI = A$, $BI = B$
   $IA = A$, $IB = B$

6. a)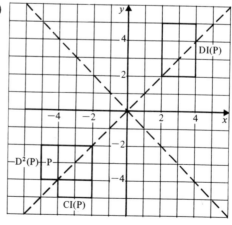

b) $CI = C$, $DI = D$,
   $D^2 = I$

7. a)

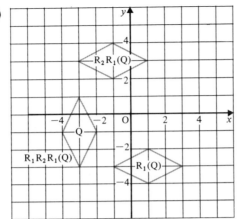

b) $R_2R_1 = R_3$
   $R_1R_2R_1 = I$

c) True

EXERCISE 14f   The work on the geometrical use of vectors will be expanded in 5A.

1.

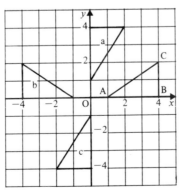

a) Rotation of $90°$ anticlockwise about O
b) Rotation of $180°$ about O
c) Rotation of $90°$ clockwise about O
d) Reflection in the x axis

2.

a) Reflection in the line $y = x$
b) Reflection in the y axis
c) Reflection in the line $y = -x$

3.

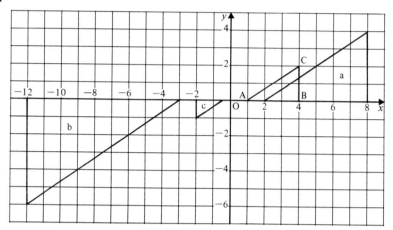

a) Enlargement centre O, scale factor 2

b) Enlargement centre O, scale factor −3

c) Enlargement centre O, scale factor $-\frac{1}{2}$

4.

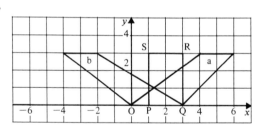

5.

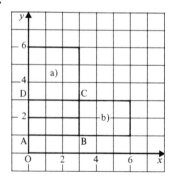

EXERCISE 14g

1. 4

2. 1

3. −2

4. 6

5. −2

6. 2

7. 7

8. 1

9. 0

10.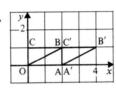

a) 2, 2   b) 1

c) 1

11.

a) 2, 2   b) 1

c) 1

12.

a) 2, 18   b) 9

c) 9

13.

a) 2, $\frac{1}{2}$ b) $\frac{1}{4}$

c) $\frac{1}{4}$

14.

a) 2, 0   b) 0

c) 0

15.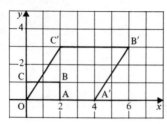

a) 2, 12   b) 6

c) 6

In questions 10 to 15, the area scale factor (b) is equal to the determinant (c)

EXERCISE 14h   **1.** Rotation of $90°$ anticlockwise about O

2. $(0,0)$, $(0,1)$, $(-1,1)$, $(-2,1)$

3. Rotation of $180°$ about O

4. Enlargement centre O, scale factor $2\frac{1}{2}$

5. $(0,0)$, $(0,1)$, $(3,1)$, $(2,1)$

6. The square becomes a line segment

7. 1. 1   **2.** 1   **3.** 1   **4.** $\frac{25}{4}$ **5.** 1   **6.** 0

8. a) A line segment   **b)** 0, 0

c) 0

9. a) 5, 5   **b)** 30

10. a) 6   **b)** 18

EXERCISE 14i   **1.** Rotation of $60°$ anticlockwise about $(1,1)$

2. Reflection in the x axis

3. An enlargement centre O, scale factor $\frac{1}{2}$

4. Translation defined by $\begin{pmatrix} -2 \\ -3 \end{pmatrix}$

5. Rotation of $180°$ about O

6.

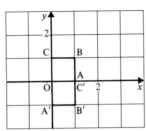

b) Rotation of 90° clockwise about O

c) Rotation of 90° anticlockwise about O

d) $\begin{pmatrix} 0 & -1 \\ 1 & 0 \end{pmatrix}$

e) The image of OA'B'C' is OABC

f) Rotation of 90° anticlockwise about O

7.

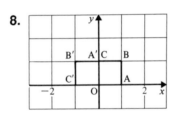

b) Enlargement centre O, scale factor 2

c) Enlargement centre O, scale factor $\frac{1}{2}$

d) $\begin{pmatrix} \frac{1}{2} & 0 \\ 0 & \frac{1}{2} \end{pmatrix}$

e) The image of OA'B'C' is OABC

f) Enlargement centre O, scale factor $\frac{1}{2}$

8.

b) Rotation of 90° anticlockwise about O

c) Rotation of 90° clockwise about O

d) $\begin{pmatrix} 0 & 1 \\ -1 & 0 \end{pmatrix}$

e) The image of OA'B'C' is OABC

f) Rotation of 90° clockwise about O

g) Yes; $\begin{pmatrix} 0 & 1 \\ -1 & 0 \end{pmatrix}$

9. i) (b) and (c)   Reflection in the line $y = x$ d) $\begin{pmatrix} 0 & -1 \\ -1 & 0 \end{pmatrix}$

ii) (b) and (c)   Reflection in the y axis   d) $\begin{pmatrix} -1 & 0 \\ 0 & 1 \end{pmatrix}$

In each case the inverse matrix is the same as the original matrix and the transformation is its own inverse.

10. i) and ii) a) The image is a line segment

b) There is no inverse transformation

EXERCISE 14k A shorter method using the inverse matrix is given here but it demands a degree of sophistication which not all pupils can command.

$$\begin{pmatrix} a & b \\ c & d \end{pmatrix} \begin{pmatrix} 2 & 3 \\ 1 & 4 \end{pmatrix} = \begin{pmatrix} 5 & 10 \\ 3 & 12 \end{pmatrix} \qquad (1)$$

The inverse of $\begin{pmatrix} 2 & 3 \\ 1 & 4 \end{pmatrix}$ is $\frac{1}{5}\begin{pmatrix} 4 & -3 \\ -1 & 2 \end{pmatrix}$

Post multiply both sides of (1)

$$\begin{pmatrix} a & b \\ c & d \end{pmatrix} \left[\begin{pmatrix} 2 & 3 \\ 1 & 4 \end{pmatrix} \times \frac{1}{5}\begin{pmatrix} 4 & -3 \\ -1 & 2 \end{pmatrix} \right] = \begin{pmatrix} 5 & 10 \\ 3 & 12 \end{pmatrix} \times \frac{1}{5}\begin{pmatrix} 4 & -3 \\ -1 & 2 \end{pmatrix}$$

$$\begin{pmatrix} a & b \\ c & d \end{pmatrix} = \begin{pmatrix} 2 & 1 \\ 0 & 3 \end{pmatrix}$$

1. $\begin{pmatrix} 1 & 0 \\ 0 & 2 \end{pmatrix}$ **3.** $\begin{pmatrix} 3 & 0 \\ 1 & 1 \end{pmatrix}$ **5.** $\begin{pmatrix} 1 & -4 \\ 0 & 3 \end{pmatrix}$

2. $\begin{pmatrix} 1 & 2 \\ 2 & 0 \end{pmatrix}$ **4.** $\begin{pmatrix} 1 & -1 \\ 0 & 5 \end{pmatrix}$ **6.** $\begin{pmatrix} 9 & -4 \\ -2 & 1 \end{pmatrix}$

7. $\begin{pmatrix} 3 & 0 \\ 0 & 2 \end{pmatrix}$ **9.** $\begin{pmatrix} 1 & 0 \\ 0 & -1 \end{pmatrix}$ **11.** $\begin{pmatrix} 0 & -1 \\ 1 & 0 \end{pmatrix}$

8. $\begin{pmatrix} 1 & 1 \\ 1 & 2 \end{pmatrix}$ **10.** $\begin{pmatrix} 0 & 1 \\ -1 & 0 \end{pmatrix}$ **12.** $\begin{pmatrix} 0 & 1 \\ 1 & 0 \end{pmatrix}$

EXERCISE 14l   **1.** a) 2   b) 5 ; Scale factor = 3

2. a) (9 , 5)   b) (−1 , 1)   c) (2 , 1)

3. a) $\begin{pmatrix} 2 & -1 \\ -3\frac{1}{2} & 2 \end{pmatrix}$ b) (1 , 2)

4. $\begin{pmatrix} y \\ x \end{pmatrix}$ Reflection in the line $y = x$

5. a) $\begin{pmatrix} x \\ 3x + y \end{pmatrix}$ **b)** $(p, \ 4p)$ **c)** 4

EXERCISE 14m **1. B**   **2. A**   **3. A**   **4. D**   **5. B**

CHAPTER 15 Quadratic Equations

EXERCISE 15a Much of this exercise can be considered orally.

1. $\left(x + 3 \right)^2$

2. $\left(a + 2 \right)^2$

3. $\left(p - 5 \right)^2$

4. $\left(s - 6 \right)^2$

5. $\left(x - \frac{5}{2} \right)^2$

6. $\left(b + \frac{3}{2} \right)^2$

7. $\left(x + \frac{9}{2} \right)^2$

8. $\left(x - \frac{1}{2} \right)^2$

9. $\left(x - \frac{1}{4} \right)^2$

10. $\left(x + 4 \right)^2$

11. $\left(x + \frac{1}{2} \right)^2$

12. $\left(x + \frac{1}{3} \right)^2$

13. $\left(p + 9 \right)^2$

14. $\left(a - \frac{2}{5} \right)^2$

15. $\left(t - \frac{3}{4} \right)^2$

16. $\left(x + b \right)^2$

17. $\left(x - c \right)^2$

18. $\left(x + \frac{b}{2a} \right)^2$

19. $\left(3x + 1 \right)^2$

20. $\left(2x - 3 \right)^2$

21. $\left(10x - 3 \right)^2$

22. $\left(3x - 4 \right)^2$

23. $\left(2x - 1 \right)^2$

24. $\left(5x + 2 \right)^2$

25. $\left(3x - 1 \right)^2$

26. $\left(2x + \frac{1}{2} \right)^2$

27. $\left(\frac{3}{2}x + \frac{2}{3} \right)^2$

EXERCISE 15b Best used as an oral exercise with the addition of home produced examples if necessary.

1. 4	**5.** $\frac{9}{4}$	**9.** $\frac{9}{16}$
2. 16	**6.** 100	**10.** $\frac{1}{4}$
3. 36	**7.** $\frac{49}{4}$	**11.** h^2
4. 49	**8.** $\frac{1}{16}$	**12.** $\frac{b^2}{4a^2}$

EXERCISE 15c This exercise may be omitted on first reading.

1. 4	**4.** 9	**7.** 4
2. 9	**5.** 4	**8.** 4
3. 25	**6.** 25	**9.** $\frac{1}{4}$

EXERCISE 15d Show that, if $x^2 = 4$, then writing $x = \pm 2$ or $\pm x = \pm 2$ gives the same information.

Most pupils need to be satisfied on this point at some time or another.

1. 2, −4	**5.** −8, −6	**9.** 5, 9
2. −2, 6	**6.** −4, 6	**10.** −8, 0
3. −2, 8	**7.** −9, 5	**11.** −8, 2
4. −16, 4	**8.** 1, 9	**12.** 3, 15

13. $-\frac{1}{2}$, $-1\frac{1}{2}$	**18.** −1, $\frac{7}{5}$	**23.** $-\frac{7}{5}$, $\frac{3}{5}$
14. $\frac{1}{2}$, $3\frac{1}{2}$	**19.** 1, $\frac{5}{3}$	**24.** $\frac{1}{2}$, 1
15. −2, 3	**20.** $-\frac{12}{7}$, $\frac{8}{7}$	**25.** $\frac{3}{9}$, $\frac{7}{9}$
16. $-\frac{3}{2}$, $\frac{5}{2}$	**21.** $-\frac{7}{2}$, $\frac{5}{2}$	**26.** $-1\frac{2}{5}$, $\frac{1}{5}$
17. $-\frac{7}{3}$, 1	**22.** −1, $\frac{11}{3}$	**27.** $-\frac{4}{7}$, 2

EXERCISE 15e Better pupils should profit by being shown how to solve a quadratic equation by completing the square even if it is subsequently discarded in favour of the formula.

1. 1, −5
2. −1, 7
3. −11, 1
4. −7.61, −0.39
5. 0.27, 3.73
6. −8.36, 0.36

7. −1.61, 5.61
8. −8.53, −0.47
9. 0.81, 6.19
10. −1.56, 2.56
11. −9.32, 0.32
12. −0.54, 7.46

13. −4.10, 1.10
14. −0.35, 2.35
15. −2.32, 0.32
16. −0.85, 2.35
17. −4.58, 0.58
18. −0.18, 1.85

19. −0.52, 1.52
20. −1.29, −0.31
21. −0.36, 2.11
22. −0.17, 1
23. −1.41, 0.41
24. −0.21, 3.21

EXERCISE 15f Pupils should be encouraged to check that the sum of the roots is equal to $-\dfrac{b}{a}$

1. −5.45, −0.55
2. −6.37, −0.63
3. −3.62, −1.38
4. −7.27, 0.27
5. −4.65, 0.65
6. −7.37, −1.63

7. −5.73, −2.27
8. −11.32, 1.32
9. −6.87, 0.87
10. −9.11, 0.11
11. −4.19, 1.19
12. −5.32, 1.32

13. 3.41, 0.59
14. 0.46, 6.54
15. 1.27, 4.73
16. −0.65, 4.65
17. −0.85, 5.85
18. 0.44, 4.56

19. 0.38, 2.62
20. −0.41, 7.41
21. −0.22, 9.22
22. −1.61, 5.61
23. −7.27, 0.27
24. −7.32, −0.68

25. −3.19, −0.31
26. −2.78, −0.72
27. −1.77, −0.57
28. −1.59, −0.16
29. −1.54, −0.26

30. 0.72, 2.78
31. 0.16, 1.59
32. 0.26, 1.54
33. −2.14, 0.47
34. −3.11, 0.11

EXERCISE 15g
1. −1.08, −5.08
2. −0.32, 2.32
3. −2.14, 0.47
4. −0.68, 0.88
5. 0.36, 1.39
6. −0.16, 4.16
7. −0.28, 1.78
8. −1.55, 0.80

9. 0.24, 2.76
10. −0.36, 1.86
11. −0.77, 3.27
12. −1.55, 0.22
13. −0.21, 1.21
14. −2.59, 0.26
15. 0.28, 0.72
16. −0.30, 0.42

EXERCISE 15h Some of the equations included in this exercise may be solved by factorising. This is deliberate since factorisation should always be attempted before resorting to the formula. Some examination boards employ a code. When they ask for the roots of a quadratic equation to be given 'correct to two decimal places', they mean 'use the formula'!

1. −2, 0.5
2. −1.58, −0.42
3. −0.67, −0.5
4. −2.19, 0.69
5. 0.28, 2.39

6. −0.33, 3
7. −0.69, 2.19
8. −1.50, 0.25
9. −1.40, 0.24
10. −0.43, 1.18

11. −1.35, 0.21
12. −0.24, 0.84
13. 0.33, 2.00
14. −0.70, −0.39
15. −0.75, 0.20

16. 1.67, 3
17. −1.29, −0.31
18. −0.39, 3.89
19. −5, 0.5
20. −0.30, 1.13

EXERCISE 15i This exercise includes demanding questions. The better pupils will enjoy tackling them, and their solution will improve the pupils' manipulative skills.

1. 0.18, 10.82
2. −1.19, 4.19
3. 0.30, 6.70
4. −4.30, −0.70

5. −4.55, 2.80
6. −0.84, 0.59
7. −4.27, 3.27
8. −3.27, 0.77

EXERCISE 15j Plenty of time spent in classroom discussion should result in more acceptable solutions.

1. 6, 7
2. 2, 4
3. 5, 6
4. 5 cm, 9 cm
5. 5 cm, 8 cm
6. 5, 8

7. 5 cm, 12 cm, 13 cm
8. 2 cm, 8 cm
9. 6 cm, 8 cm, 10 cm
10. 6 cm, 8 cm
11. 7, 12
12. 8, 11

13. 4 cm, 9 cm
14. a) 12 cm
    b) 7 cm
15. 13 cm by 6 cm
16. 24 cm, 5 cm

EXERCISE 15k **1.** 1.13, 8.87
2. 1.17, 7.83

3. 0.05 or 19.95
4. 6.22, 3.22

5. 8.46 cm, 6.46 cm, 5.46 cm
6. Parallel sides are 4 cm and 10 cm
Distance between them is 6 cm
7. 10 cm × 5 cm × 3 cm
8. 38 years

EXERCISE 15l An interesting exercise for the better pupil.

1. 60 mph
2. 30 p
3. £6, £9
4. £1 ≡ 10 F
5. Rectangle 9 cm × 6 cm, square of side 3 cm
or Rectangle $\frac{27}{7}$ cm × $\frac{18}{7}$ cm, square of side $\frac{51}{7}$ cm
6. 42

CHAPTER 16 Using Money

Revise basic percentage work before working this chapter. Much of the work in this chapter is optional. However it does provide practice in arithmetic and some of the topics covered are useful general knowledge.

EXERCISE 16a
1. a) £17   b) £17.24
2. a) £1.70   b) £1.72
3. a) £200   b) £215.52
4. a) 40 p   b) 43 p
5. a) £37   b) £38.79
6. a) £25   b) £22.72
7. a) 50 p   b) 45 p
8. a) 20 p   b) 18 p
9. a) £3   b) £2.72
10. a) £19   b) £17.32
11. a) £1.20   b) £1.25

12. a) £4   b) £4.17
13. a) 10 p   b) 10 p
14. a) £5   b) £5.21
15. a) 40 p   b) 38 p
16. a) £2   b) £2.08
17. a) £4   b) £4
18. a) £8   b) £8.33
19. a) £20   b) £20.83
20. a) £1.30   b) £1.33
21. a) £3   b) £3.08

22. 9.67 Ff
23. 5.27 Ff
24. 207 L
25. 9.17 pta
26. 109 L

27. 33.83 Ff
28. 34.27 Ff
29. 5172 L
30. 412.5 pta
31. 3055 L

32. 17 380 L
33. 348 pta
34. 11.2 DM
35. 9.4 DM

36. 5.4 DM
37. £4.80
38. £2.10
39. 65 p

40.

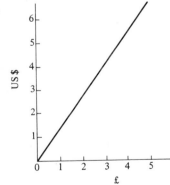

a) 3.50 $
b) 6.70 $
c) £3

EXERCISE 16b   Useful table reading practice.

1. £1 = 1.929 C$
2. 1 DM = 674.9 L
3. 100 B Fr = 398.2 yen :   1 B Fr = 3.982 yen
4. 1 H Fl = 0.334 $
5. 1 $ = 214.6 yen
6. 1 S Fr = £0.325
7. 1 $ = £0.708
8. 100 B Fr = 1.855 $:   1 B Fr = 0.018 55 $
9. 1 DM = 0.376 $
10. 1 H Fl = £0.236

EXERCISE 16c   Point out that looking at 'Bank buys and bank sells' columns, it appears at first sight that you get better value on cashing in foreign currency, but don't be misled!

1. 370 DM
2. £64.10
3. £400
4. £357.10
5. 112 500 pta
6. £62.67
7. £347.40
8. £7.59
9. £50.75
10. £181

EXERCISE 16d   Point out that the interest payable on an investment is only one factor that influences choice of investment. Ease of access to capital and withdrawal facilities also matter.

1. a) £105.06   b) £104.06
2. a) £109.20   b) £109.20
3. a) £214.25   b) 7.12%
4. a) £110.25   b) 10.25%   c) £121.55
5. £119.25;   not as good as the Savings Certificates
6. £200;   £1169.86
7. The local authority bond pays £90 a year; the savings account gives £87.75 interest a year; the bond gives the greater return

EXERCISE 16e   1. 9.86%   2. 12.3%   3. 6.25%   4. 8.57%   5. 20%   6. 27.3%   7. 7.5%

8. The net rate on the post office account is 5.6%, so a tax payer gets 0.4% more from the building society
9. 10% gross is equivalent to 6.7% net of standard rate tax.
   a) net account, by £26 a year
   b) gross account, by £40 a year

EXERCISE 16f Nos. 1-4 can be worked before discussing multiplying factors. If more simple problems are required before embarking on multiplying factors, Exercise 5g in 3A can be used.

1. £102.50	**6.** 1.851	**11.** 0.4344
2. £561.80	**7.** 0.2725	**12.** 0.1880
3. £779.14	**8.** 0.6302	**13.** £3173.75
4. £496.50	**9.** 1.685	
5. 2.476	**10.** 16.37	

14. a) £11 655.26   b) £21 306.27
15. £11 390.81
16. a) £4962.81   b) £4603.02
17. a) £3711.71   b) £4235.94
18. a) £48 400   b) £64 400
19. a) £27 200   b) £31 700

20. £100.57   **22.** £14.40
21. a) £1100 b) £900   **23.** 2 400 000

EXERCISE 16g

1. £18.51	**7.** £803	**13.** £900	**18.** 9
2. £37.40	**8.** £1651	**14.** 4000	**19.** 3
3. 3582	**9.** £609.90	**15.** £50	**20.** 7
4. £171.80	**10.** £823.60	**16.** 4	**21.** 14%
5. 8630	**11.** £200	**17.** 8	**22.** 3
6. £1019	**12.** £500		

EXERCISE 16h It is worth mentioning charge cards as well as credit cards. For example American Express is a charge card: on such cards the monthly balance has to be paid in full; there is no extended credit (the card company usually charges a fixed annual amount for the card so they get their money from that rather than from interest).

1. £287.50
2. a) £61 500 b) £39 600
3. a) £387.60 b) £116 280
4. £291.67
5. Yes: monthly repayments of £82.50 needed to cover interest
6. £626   **7.** £128
8. a) £5 b) £300
9. a) £10 129.68 b) £9500.10
10. Rental costs £4320 and buying and paying for repairs costs £4360 so buying would cost £40 more
11. £18.11
12. No: he only had £26.80 credit available

CHAPTER 17   Gradients and Areas

If further practice in finding areas and gradients is required, use graphs drawn for chapter 5 or any other previously drawn graphs.
(The graphs provided for these answers are to give an idea of the shape required. They are drawn to smaller scales than those asked for in the questions.)

EXERCISE 17a   Drawing a curve on the board and moving a ruler along the curve in the direction of the tangent, helps show how the gradient at any point is the gradient of the tangent.

1.

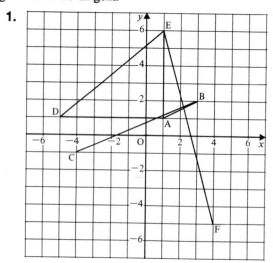

a) $\frac{1}{2}$

b) $\frac{3}{7}$

c) $\frac{5}{6}$

d) $-\frac{11}{3}$

e) 0

f) not possible

2. a) -3 b) 0   c) $\frac{1}{2}$ d) 2

3.

x	0	1	2	3	4	5	6	7	8
y	0	0.1	0.4	0.9	1.6	2.5	3.6	4.9	6.4

a) 0.6

c) $\frac{1}{5}$, $\frac{4}{5}$, $\frac{6}{5}$

4.

x	1	1.5	2	3	4	5	6	7	8
y	10	6.6	5	3.3	2.5	2	1.7	1.4	1.3

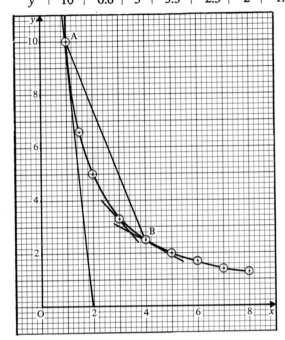

a) -2.5
b) -10, -0.6
c) -1.1

EXERCISE 17b

1. a) i) 29   ii) 33
b) 33 or 44 (must be a whole number)
c) $\frac{21}{4}$;   the number of ripe strawberries is increasing by $5\frac{1}{4}$ a day on average
d) -6;   the number of ripe strawberries is falling at 6 per day

2.

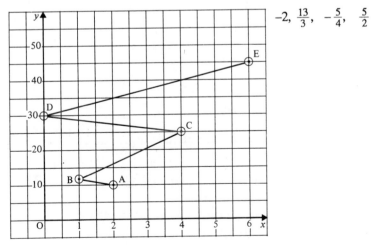

$-2, \dfrac{13}{3}, \; -\dfrac{5}{4}, \; \dfrac{5}{2}$

3.

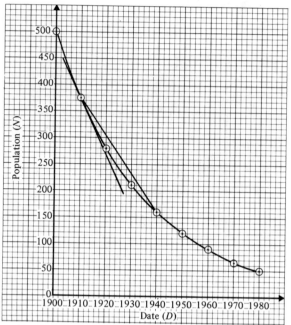

a) −7.2; from 1910 to 1940; the population decreased by an average of 7.2 people per year

b) −11; in 1910; the population was decreasing by 11 people a year

4.

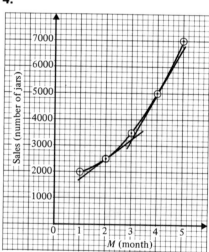

a) 800; in month 2, sales increased by 800 jars a month

b) 1800; in month 4, sales increased by 1800 jars a month

5.

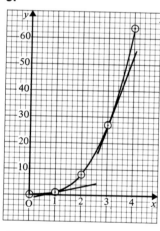

a) 3

b) 27

6.

x	0	1	2	2.5	3	4
y	0	9	12	11.25	9	0

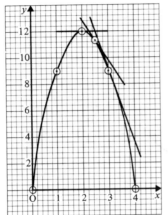

a) 0
b) −3
c) −6

EXERCISE 17c

1. a) 6.25 cm²
2. a) 10 cm²
3. a) 16.75 cm²
4. a) 79 cm²

b) 6.25 m² (25 squares)
b) 160 m² (40 squares)
b) 67 km² (67 squares)
b) 78.5 cm²

EXERCISE 17d Remind pupils of the significance of *m* and *c* in the operation $y = mx + c$ and insist on sketches, not accurate plots.

1. 12 sq units
2. 12.5 sq units
3. 36 sq units
4. 9 sq units

5. 78 sq units
6. 112 sq units
7. 60 sq units
8. 33.75 sq units

EXERCISE 17e Sketch graphs are all that is needed for this exercise. This method can be formalised into the trapezium rule:

$$area \approx \frac{1}{2}d\{sum\ of\ 1st\ and\ last\ ordinate + twice\ sum\ of\ the\ other\ ordinates\}$$

where *d* is the width of each strip.

1. a) 26 sq units   b) 27 sq units
   The answer to b) is probably nearer the true value
2. 14 sq units
   Using 2 strips gives 12.5 sq units: less accurate because the second strip leaves out a larger area than the extra included by the first trapezium

3. 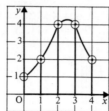   11.5 sq units

4. 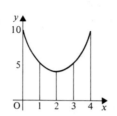   26 sq units and this is greater than the true value

5. a) 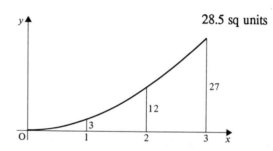   28.5 sq units

b) 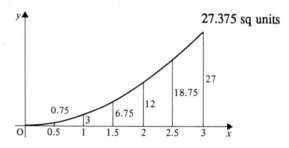   27.375 sq units

6. a)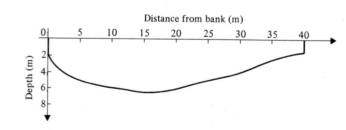

b) 183.75 m²   c) 460 litres   d) 1 654 000 litres

CHAPTER 18   Travel Graphs ═══════════════════════════════

EXERCISE 18a   Revises units and change of units. A useful memory aid for the relationship

between distance, speed and time is

1. a) 0.55 km/min   b) 33 000 m/h
2. a) 0.1 km/s   b) 6000 m/min
3. a) $\frac{2}{3}$ miles/min   b) $\frac{1}{90}$ miles/s
4. a) 0.025 km/s   b) 25 m/s
5. a) 360 000 m/h   b) 360 km/h

6. 2500 m   11. $1\frac{2}{3}$ miles
7. 0.375 m/s   12. 50 m/s
8. 30 m.p.h.   13. 0.4 m/s
9. 30 minutes   14. 3.6 km
10. 0.96 km   15. 40 seconds

EXERCISE 18b   If it is thought desirable, the distinction between distance and displacement can be made now. The word displacement is not used in this chapter. A common mistake is to use place names on the vertical axis: this is confusing because pupils may tend to think of those points on the vertical axis as 'places' to get to and may even try to make the graph come back to the vertical axis.

The graphs given in the following answers are drawn to scales smaller than asked for in the questions. They are provided to give an idea of the shape required.

1.

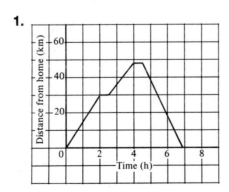

6.9 hours
(6 hours 54 mins)

2.

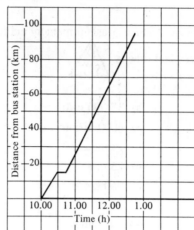

95 km

3.

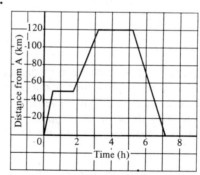

a) 62.5 km/h
b) 2 hours

4.

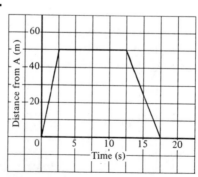

17.5 seconds

5.

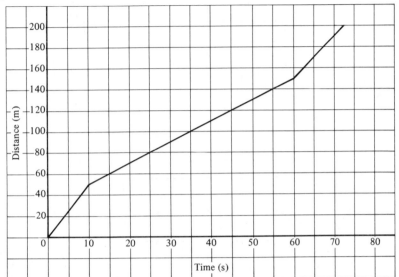

72.5 seconds

6.

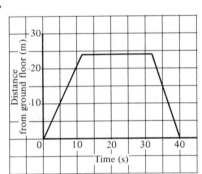

a) 24 m
b) 3 m/s

EXERCISE 18c

1. a) 12 km/h   b) 13.9 km/h   (to 3 s.f.)

2. a) 30.4 km/h   (to 3 s.f.)   b) 35.2 km/h   (to 3 s.f.)

3. a) $33\frac{1}{3}$ km/h   b) $33\frac{1}{3}$ km/h

4. a) 5.71 m/s   (to 3 s.f.)   b) 5.71 m/s   (to 3 s.f.)

5. a) 2.83 m/s   (to 3 s.f.)   b) 2.76 m/s   (to 3 s.f.)

6. a) 1.2 m/s   b) 1.2 m/s

EXERCISE 18d   **1.**

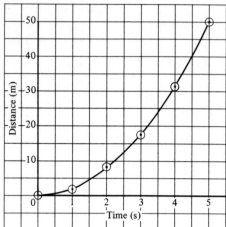

a) 12.5 m
b) 6 m/s
c) 10 m/s

2.

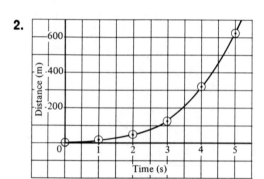

a) 456 m
b) 80 m/s
c) 185 m/s

EXERCISE 18e   **1.** a) speed   b) velocity   c) velocity   d) speed
e) speed   f) velocity   g) velocity

2. a) $\underset{\text{A}}{\text{A}}\ \overset{\text{2 m/s}}{\longleftarrow}\ \underset{\text{B}}{\text{B}}$

b) $\underset{\text{A}}{\text{A}}\ \overset{\text{4 m/s}}{\longrightarrow}\ \underset{\text{B}}{\text{B}}$

c) $\underset{\text{A}}{\text{A}}\ \overset{\text{10 m/s}}{\longleftarrow}\ \underset{\text{B}}{\text{B}}$

d) A ——————•—————— B

3. a) 10 m/s   b) 10 m/s   c) 7.5 m/s
d) −7.5 m/s   e) 6 m/s

4. The ball moves with velocity 0.8 m/s for 5 seconds then with velocity − 0.4 m/s (i.e. in the opposite direction with speed 0.4 m/s) for 5 seconds and then stops.

5. (b) , (d) , (e)

EXERCISE 18f　Point out that drawing a tangent by eye is neither easy or accurate so that answers obtained are very approximate. However it is the only method available at this stage.

1. a) 8 m/s　　b) 8 m/s　　　c) 16 m/s
2. a) 140 m/s　b) 95 m/s　　　c) 60 m/s　d) 93.75 m/s (94 m/s)

3.

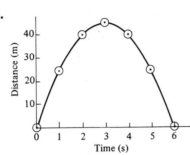

　a) 6 sec after leaving it
　b) 15 m/s
　c) 17.5 m/s
　d) 20 m/s
　e) −10 m/s
　f) −20 m/s

4. a) 15 m/s　　b) 20 m/s　　c) 5 m/s　　d) 31 m　　e) −15m/s

5. a)

t	0	1	2	3	4
$8t$	0	8	16	24	32
$2t^2$	0	2	8	18	32
d	0	6	8	6	0

b)

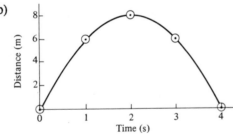

c) 0,　−4 m/s　　　　　　　　d) 8 m

EXERCISE 18g　**1.** 30 m/s,　60 seconds
　　　　　　　　2. a) 4 m/s　　　　　b) 60 m/s　　　　　　c) 120 m/s
　　　　　　　　3. 15 seconds
　　　　　　　　4. 2 m/s²
　　　　　　　　5. a) 90 km/h　　　　b) 300 km/h　　　　　c) 22.5 km/h
　　　　　　　　6. 14 km/h/s ≡ 14 km/minute² (accept any units, e.g. $3\frac{8}{9}$ m/s²)
　　　　　　　　7. $2\frac{7}{9}$ m/s²

EXERCISE 18h

1. a) 2.5 m/s²

b) the acceleration becomes less

c) 2 seconds

d) 2 seconds

e) 7.5 m/s²

f) 10 seconds

2. a) 10 km/min²

b) 15 km/min

c) 27.5 km/min

d) 2.5 km/min²

3. a) 5 km/min /h $\equiv \frac{1}{12}$ km/min² $\equiv$ 300 km/h²

b) 15 km/h

c) 3 minutes

d) zero

e) 5 km/h/min $= \frac{1}{12}$ km/min² $\equiv$ 300 km/h²

4.

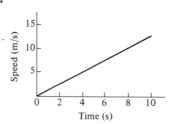

7.

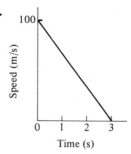

5.

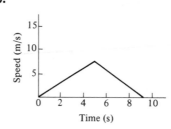

8.

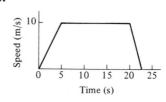

6.

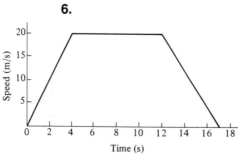

9.

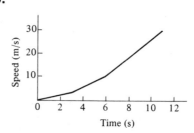

10.

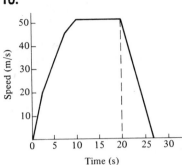

11.

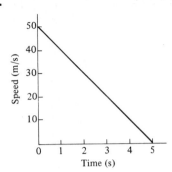

12.

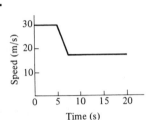

13.

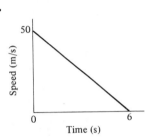

EXERCISE 18i

1. a) 15 m/s^2 b) 7.5 m/s^2 c) 1 sec   d) 15 m   e) 67.5 m

2. a) 115 m   b) 35 km   c) $\frac{1}{6}$ km

3. a) 800 m/s^2 b) 3 m
    c) 1200 m/s^2 d) 4 m
    e) 4000 m/s^2 f) 0.3125 m

4. a) 0.185 m/s^2 b) 1000 m

5. a) 0.017 m/s^2 b) 5 m/s   c) 0.025 m/s^2 d) 300 m   e) 420 m

6. a) 0.667 m/s^2 b) 1 m/s^2 c) 75 m   d) 50 m   e) 475 m

An alternative way of saying that the gradient of the tangent gives acceleration is to point out that the gradient of the distance–time curve gives the velocity, so it is reasonable that the gradient of the velocity–time curve gives the acceleration.

EXERCISE 18j

1. a) 5 m/s   b) decelerating   c) 38.5 m

2. a) 98 m (using 5 strips)
    b) i) T   ii) T   iii) F   iv) T

3.

t	0	1	2	3	4
v	0	1	8	27	64

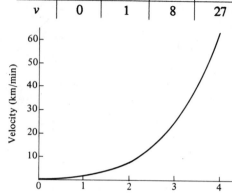

a) 12 km/min^2
b) 16 km/min^2
c) after 2.7 minutes
d) 22.5 km (using 3 strips)
e) 45.5 km (using 1 strip)

4.

a) 9 m/s,   3 seconds after release
b) 7 m/s
c) 4 m/s^2
d) zero
e) 35 m (using 6 strips)

EXERCISE 18k

1. B	**3. D**	**5. D**	**7. D**	**9. A**
2. B	**4. B**	**6. C**	**8. A**	**10. A**

CHAPTER 19   Variation

Much use can be made of real life situations in this chapter.

EXERCISE 19a

1. $y = 3x$

2. $q = p^2$

3. $V = x^2$

4. $r = \sqrt{A}$

5. $xy = 24$ or $y = \dfrac{24}{x}$

6. $s = \dfrac{1}{10}r$

7. $y = 4x^2$

8. $pq = -36$ or $q = -\dfrac{36}{p}$

9. $A = \dfrac{1}{2}L^2$

10. $A = \dfrac{1}{3}b^2$

11.

x	2	3	4	5
y	8	27	64	125

EXERCISE 19b **1.**

x	2	4	7	8	9.5
y	20	40	70	80	95

$y = 10x$

2.

r	1	3	5	6	8
C	6	18	30	36	48

$C = 6r$

3.

Number of units of electricity used (n)	100	120	142	260	312	460
Total cost in pence (C)	600	720	852	1560	1872	2760

$C = 6n$ The cost of one unit of electricity

4.

Number of oranges bought (X)	2	4	7	9	11	15
Total cost in pence (Y)	20	40	70	90	110	150

$Y = 10X$ The cost of one orange

5. a) 9   b) 16   **9.** a) 21   b) 40

6. a) $\frac{3}{2}$ b) 20   **10.** a) 24   b) 15

7. a) 21   b) 7   **11.** a) 15   b) 8

8. a) 6   b) 3

EXERCISE 19c **1.**

x	0	2	3	4	5	8
y	0	12	27	48	75	192

$y = 3x^2$

2.

t	2	4	5	6	10
s	20	80	125	180	500

$s = 5t^2$

3.

x	−3	−1	0	2	4	7
y	36	4	0	16	48	196

$y = 4x^2$

4. a) 32   b) $\pm\frac{1}{2}$ **5.** a) $\frac{3}{4}$ b) $\pm\frac{1}{3}$ **6.** a) 108   b) ± 8

7.

H	2	4	6	8	10
V	2	16	54	128	250

$V = \frac{1}{4}H^3$

8.

x	3	6	9	12	15
y	9	72	243	576	1125

$y = \frac{1}{3}x^3$

9. a) 24　　b) 6
10. a) 216　　b) 1
11. a) 108　　b) 2

12.

R	0	1	4	9	25
V	0	4	8	12	20

$V = 4\sqrt{R}$

13. a) 2　　b) 900

14. No;

$\sqrt{x}$	1	2	3	4	5
y	1	2	3	4	5

yes;　$y = \sqrt{x}$

15. No;　$y = \frac{1}{2}x^3$

EXERCISE 19d

1. $CN = 500$ or $N = \dfrac{500}{C}$

2. $CN = 720$ or $C = \dfrac{720}{N}$

3. $PV = 120$ or $V = \dfrac{120}{P}$

4. $xy = 12$ or $y = \dfrac{12}{x}$

5. $xy = 72$ or $y = \dfrac{72}{x}$

6. $xy = 1$　or $y = \dfrac{1}{x}$

EXERCISE 19e

1. $xy = 36$ or $y = \dfrac{36}{x}$

2. $y = \dfrac{36}{x^2}$

3. $q = \dfrac{60}{\sqrt{p}}$

4. a) 4　　b) 20　　c) –10

5. a) $\frac{4}{3}$　　b) 16

6. a) 10　　　　b) 40

7. a) 6　　　　b) 0

8. a) 25　　　b) 10

9. a) 4　　　　b) 12

10. a) 56　　　b) 2

11. a) 2　　b) 2　　c) 3　　d) –1　　e) $\frac{1}{2}$　　f) 1

EXERCISE 19f

1. a) 1　　b) 1　　c) $\frac{25}{4}$

2. a) 21　　b) 6

3. a) $y = \frac{3}{4}x^3$　b) 6　　c) 2

4. a) 14　　b) 3

5. a) 8　　b) ±3

6.

x	0	1	2	4	8
y	0	0.25	1	4	16

7.

s	0	4	9	16	64
t	0	0.5	0.75	1	2

8. a) 2   b) 3   c) 1   d) −1

EXERCISE 19g   Your science colleagues will be most appreciative of the amount of time and effort that goes into this exercise!

1. a) 2.4 N   b) $E = 8.3F$

2. 45° C

3. c) 1.2

4. a) Fifth one   c) $d = 4t$; 4 m s^{-1}

5. c) 10

EXERCISE 19h   Before leaving this chapter pupils should be well aware that mathematically similar solids are very deceptive in terms of the ratio of their volumes or capacities compared with their heights or any other corresponding linear dimensions. This could lead on to discussion of unit pricing and 'best buys'.

1. a) 4 kg   b) 25 cm   **6.** a) doubles   b) × 5

2. 64 m   **7.** a) 0.216 litre   b) 20 cm

3. a) $\frac{8}{5}$ b) $112\frac{1}{2}$ **8.** a) 3   b) 120

4. a) 25 cm   b) 4.8 N   **9.** a) 40 mph   b) 12 mph

5. a) £320   b) 4.5 m   **10.** a) 2   b) $\frac{1}{2}$ c) 4   d) 8

11. a) +25 %   b) −20 %   c) $56\frac{1}{4}$ %

CHAPTER 20   General Revision Exercises

The exercises in this chapter comprise a mixed selection of examination type questions. They cover work from earlier books as well as topics from this book.

All answers given to 3 s.f. unless instructed otherwise.

EXERCISE 20a

1. a) £9.74   b) $4\frac{3}{8}$

2. a) $2x(x-3)$ b) $(x-1)(x-3)$ c) $(x-5)(x+2)$

3. a) $\frac{6}{7}$ b) 3,   2   c) $x = 3$, $y = -1$

4. a) $8 - 5x$ b) $\frac{4}{9}$ c) $\dfrac{x+2}{6}$

5. £35 431.22

6. $\frac{4}{9}$, $\frac{4}{9}$

7.

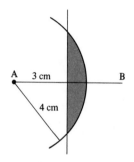

8. $y = \dfrac{144}{x}$ a) 36   b) 16

9.

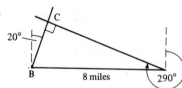

Distance from A :   7.52 miles
Distance from B :   2.74 miles

10. a) $-\frac{1}{2}$ b) $y = 3 - \frac{1}{2}x$ c) 3 square units

EXERCISE 20b

1. a) 18.30   b) 15.00

2. a) 75   b) $\frac{1}{5}$ or 1

     c) When $t = \frac{1}{5}$ the ball is 1 m from A going up and when $t = 1$ the ball is 1 m from A going down

     d) $u = \dfrac{s + 5t^2}{t}$

3. a) $15x^5$ b) $\dfrac{3x + 7}{10}$ c) 5

4.

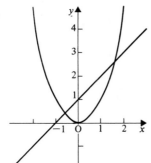

a) $x \approx -0.5$, $x \approx 1.5$
b) $x = -0.62$, $x = 1.62$

5. $x = -6$, $y = 4$
6. a) both 19.1 cm to 3 s.f.
  b) $34.9°$ to 1 d.p.

7. a) 30 b) 16 c) 9 d) 10

8.

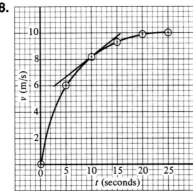

a) 7.5 m/s
b) 0.3 m/s/s
c) 50.5 m (using two strips)

9. a) 3.6 cm b) 32 cm³
10. $x = 70°$, $y = 35°$, $z = 55°$

EXERCISE 20c **1.** a) 112 km b) 70 miles
  2. a) $x = 3$ b) $x = 3.4$, $y = 1.8$
  3. a) $50x + 30y = 320$ or $5x + 3y = 32$
   b) $x + y = 8$ c) $x + y < 10$
   d) $50x + 30y > 500$ or $5x + 3y > 50$
  4. a) 5 b) -3 c) 3
  5. 0.42, 3.58

6.

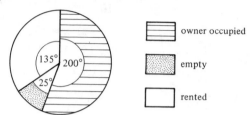

7. a)

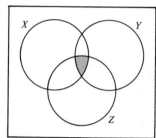

b)

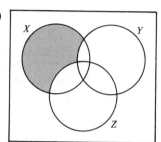

c)

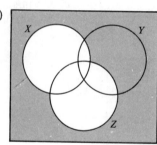

d)

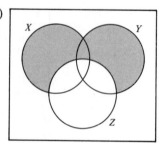

8. $\frac{3}{5}$, $\frac{7}{12}$

9.

$\frac{1}{4}$ scale

10.

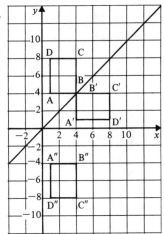

$\frac{1}{2}$ scale

c) reflection in x-axis

EXERCISE 20d

1. a) 0.001 53   b) i) 1.53×10^{-3} ii) 0.002

2. a) $\begin{pmatrix} -1 & 16 \\ -5 & 3 \end{pmatrix}$ b) $\begin{pmatrix} 10 & 33 \\ -2 & 24 \end{pmatrix}$ c) 18

3. a) 8   b) 6.37 to 3 s.f.   c) 7

4. 41.3 m to 3 s.f.

5. a) $\dfrac{7t - 4}{(t + 3)(t - 2)}$ b) 1.73, -0.93

6. a) $x = 60$,   regular hexagon

   b) BC $= 17.5$ m, $\hat{ACB} = 59.0°$

7. $\triangle$ABC and $\triangle$YZX (S A S); $\triangle$PQR and $\triangle$TUS (A A S)

8. $22 - 4x$ a) $100x$ b) $150x$ c) $5(22 - 4x)$

   $100x + 150x + 5(22 - 4x) = 800$, $x = 3$; $3 \times £1$ coins,

   9×50 p coins, 10×5 p coins

9.

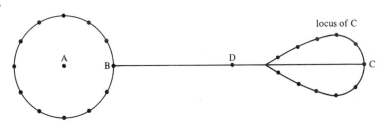

locus of C

10.

A	1	4	9	16	25
R	0.2	0.4	0.6	0.8	1

$R = (0.2)\sqrt{A}, \quad A = 100$

EXERCISE 20e   **1.** £ 48.40

2. a) $(x-3)(x+3)$ b) $3x(y-2x)$ c) $2(x-3)(x+1)$

3. a) £10   b) £12.50   c) £12

4. a) $\frac{1}{12}$ b) $\frac{5}{9}$ c) $c = \dfrac{b}{ab-1}$

6. a) 10 000 m^2 i.e. 1 hectare

   b) i) 4 cm   ii) 6.5 cm   iii) 9 cm   iv) $8\frac{7}{8}$ cm^2

7. $x^2 + (x+2)^2 = 164; \quad 8, \ 10$

8. a) 14 00   b) 10 00,   14 43 mins

   c) 00 50,   2 h 49 min

9. a) true   b) false   c) true   d) true

10. a) i) 4.77 cm   ii) 715 cm^3 b) i) G   ii) E   iii) 60 cm^3